ZOOLOGICAL ILLUSTRATION

Zoological Illustration

an essay towards
a history of printed
zoological pictures

David Knight

Senior Lecturer in History of Science,
University of Durham

DAWSON • ARCHON BOOKS

First Published in 1977
© David Knight 1977

Wm Dawson & Son Ltd, Cannon House
Folkstone, Kent, England

Archon Books, The Shoe String Press Inc
995 Sherman Avenue, Hamden,
Connecticut 06514, USA

British Library Cataloging in Publication Data

Knight, David
    Zoological illustration.
    1. Zoological illustration 2. Animals in art
    I. Title
    743'.6'09   QL46.5

ISBN 0-7129-0786-6
ARCHON ISBN 0 208 01720 8
LC 77–30385

Printed litho in Great Britain
by W & J Mackay Limited, Chatham

For Marcus, Teresa, Susannah, Jacob, & Harriet

Acknowledgements

I would like to thank Dr Ian Doyle and Mr David Burnett of Durham University Library, who arranged for much of the photography to be done; Messrs Hartshorn and Kitching, who took most of the photographs; Dr Stacey of Durham University for spending some time interpreting various electron microscope photographs to me; and the library staff at Durham, at the Royal Institution, and at the Bodleian Library.

Plate 45, Myofibrils in white muscle fibre: goldfish, flexor pinnae pectoralis Glutaraldehyde fixation × 28,000, is reproduced from Y. Uehara, G. R. Campbell and G. Burnstock, *Muscle and its Innervation: An Atlas of Fibre Structure*, Edward Arnold, London 1976, by permission.

Contents

Note: each chapter is followed by a bibliography.

Illustrations

'The thing that is difficult about painting living things is how to grasp and express their individuality.'

Ukai Uchiyama, *Sumi-e*, tr. D. Kenny (Osaka, 1971), p. 35.

'The chief object of all zoological plates, [is] that of affording sure means of recognising specimens on comparison.'

Alfred Newton, *A Dictionary of Birds* (London, 1893–97), introduction, p. 25.

'We see distinctly only what we know thoroughly.'

Josef Wolf's maxim.

1

The Purpose of
Zoological Illustration

There are many reasons why people paint, and enjoy, pictures of animals. A picture may remind us of a favourite dog or cat; if it is a hunting print, or a painting of highland cows, it may recall a holiday or revive nostalgia; it may show us what curious creatures are to be found in foreign countries, or make us look more carefully at those around us; and it may simply help us to decide whether we are in the presence of a bullfinch or chaffinch, or of a zebra or quagga. The animal kingdom presents exciting challenges to the artist. To indicate life and movement, to catch the brilliant colours and strange forms of birds, butterflies and fishes, to imitate the play of light on a pigeon's breast, or to illustrate clearly the curious contrivances whereby a fly can suck blood from a thick-skinned creature, all require skill and courage. Pictures of animals will not be convincing unless the artist has looked carefully at living creatures and has some idea of the structure of bones and muscles; for in animals every part has its function, and a stiffly-posed stuffed skin may look very unlike the living animal.

In this book we are not concerned with the whole range of animal pictures but only with published zoological illustrations. Since the eighteenth century, when the idea of putting works of art in museums became popular, philosophers of art have urged that one ought to dismiss the question of the artist's intention when contemplating a painting or a piece of sculpture. They would argue that the works in a gallery, be they medieval altarpieces, Japanese woodcuts, African sculptures, portraits, or modern abstracts, should be judged on purely aesthetic criteria without reference to either their history or to the function they were intended to perform (which was rarely that of

1

edifying visitors to museums). Such a view has its advantages, and no doubt too much background and anecdote about pictures and artists can interfere with appreciation of a work of art on its own merits, but is inappropriate in the case of published zoological illustrations. All of them have a context and they cannot be properly understood or even enjoyed if they are removed from it.

In a published work, the artist's intentions are more obvious than in a single canvas and may even be stated in the text, although often some of the most important conventions are taken for granted at any time and are not made explicit in words. During the history of printed books, zoological theory and aesthetic fashion have changed greatly, and with them has changed what is demanded of a scientific illustration. Techniques of pictorial reproduction have also altered greatly, so that what can be demanded is different at different times. Thus zoological illustrations gained in liveliness with the nineteenth-century convention that paintings of nature ought to be done at any rate partly out of doors, and again with the broadening of zoological interest from classification of creatures to study of their behaviour; while in the seventeenth century the use of copperplates meant that finer detail could be shown than on the woodcuts of Renaissance books.

Many zoological illustrations are therefore splendid examples of fine art, and can be appreciated and enjoyed even when cut out of their books and hung on the wall. This is a kind of bonus; the artist designed the picture for scientific purposes, which imposed certain constraints upon him, and yet it can give us a pure aesthetic pleasure when removed from its context. Nevertheless it is not only as bibliophiles that we should deplore the cutting-up of old zoological books so that the pictures from them can be sold. There have indeed been books which were no more than collections of animal pictures (as opposed to zoological illustrations) in which the text was either absent or of no importance. With works of this character there would be little crime involved in dismembering them, and framing the plates so that they could be more easily seen. Such books are however unusual, and most collections of pictures even without accompanying text do amount to more than the sum of their parts having been assembled with some definite end in view.

Thus a book might illustrate all the members of a genus known at a certain time thereby casting light on the extent of the knowledge and the methods of classification at that time; or it might illustrate a particular collection in the possession of a private individual or a public museum; or it might illustrate exotic creatures only recently discovered. Thus John Edward Gray of the British Museum published between 1830 and 1835 his *Indian Zoology*, consisting of plates engraved from drawings made from life by native artists in India for General Hardwicke, F.R.S. Many of the animals depicted were described for science and named by Gray; the book is therefore more than simply a collection of some of the largest and most handsome zoological illustrations that had ever appeared in England. Despite the absence of text, therefore, the book is a

2

source of information on one man's collection and also on the status and methods of natural history in British India and in London.

Ornate works with little or no text often contain a list of subscribers: and this again helps us to place the book in its context, because we can see who wanted it. Very handsome and expensive books were naturally beyond the means of most men of science even when, like John Gould's *Birds of Australia* of 1840–8, they were of great importance because they depicted and described many new species and also the whole aspect of a fauna. Patrons of science and various libraries and institutions bought the set; and Gould was in fact careful to describe his birds in the publications of learned societies as well as in his magnificent folios. From a list of subscribers we can go some way to determining whether the illustrations were intended to adorn a coffee-table, or its earlier equivalent, or to advance zoological knowledge too.

Like the vast majority of illustrated zoological works, Gould's books contained a text giving the various names by which the creature was known, in English and in the appropriate vernacular, and its scientific name and synonyms if any. This last point demanded some research in earlier works because in zoology the earliest name given in accordance with the binomial system of Linnaeus (the first Latin word denoting the genus, and the second the species) is its valid name, and any other names it may subsequently have been given are mere synonyms — perhaps given in ignorance of the first naming, or because the new specimen looked rather different from the 'type' to

3

2   **Blue jays, from Audubon's *Birds of America* (1827–38)**

4

which the original name was given. Gould also reported where the creature had been found, and described in his own or the discoverer's words its habitat and its behaviour.

This was not a new idea of Gould's, but had long been the norm even in works like his where the illustrations were really the main point of the book; and where the tension, always present in natural history illustration, between doing a striking picture and a clear diagram was resolved in favour of the first alternative. In Gould's volumes, the text is bound in with the plates, though as in all fine books there is nothing on the back of any illustration that might show through. Audubon's *Ornithological Biography*, which forms the text of his *Birds of America* of 1827–38, on the other hand was a separate publication so that relatively impecunious ornithologists could read the descriptions (by Audubon, with considerable assistance from William MacGillivray of Edinburgh) even though they could not afford the pictures; and there were other works in which a folio of plates was accompanied by an octavo volume of text. Even in these cases, the pictures were not really expected to be used without the text, although the reverse was possible. Zoological illustration is best seen as a region where text and pictures complement each other; and in this book we shall be looking at zoological plates in relation to the history of zoology rather than assessing them by purely aesthetic criteria. The context as much as the content of the illustrations will be our concern.

Because of this particular approach, we shall not be simply concerned with great or fine books such as those we have so far mentioned. Bird books particularly ever since the eighteenth century have been popular with book collectors, and there is a considerable secondary literature about them. There are also a number of works on the history of zoology, with a narrative or a bibliographical emphasis. This book is intended to fill a gap between these two groups; it is directed to the question, 'What function in science have zoological illustrations played at different times from the Renaissance to the twentieth century?' Within our five chapters we shall be discussing illustrated books, or articles from journals, which are particularly interesting or are representative: for in history it is both the novel phenomenon and the norm (or what was typical of a period) which should be studied to give us a proper perspective. Following each of the chapters are book lists of primary sources and of recent publications which cast light upon them. Not all of these will have been discussed in the text, for to do so would have made it into a mere catalogue; whereas it is intended to be an historical and bibliographical account of the changing role of zoological illustration.

We shall therefore be concerned with illustrated works as sources for the history of zoology. Naturally there have been many very important zoological works which have contained no zoological illustrations — the most dramatic example being Darwin's *Origin of Species* of 1859. By confining ourselves to illustrated works, therefore, we shall not get a complete perspective on the

5

history of the science; but we shall get a grand view, and may find that we see things that have been missed by those who have concentrated either exclusively upon the splendid folios, or upon the more austere, technical, and theoretical publications. Even in the rigorously disciplined structure of the sciences, a new perspective is valuable; in history this is also the case, and there the more explanations we have of a phenomenon — provided they are firmly based upon the sources — the happier we should be. From no single viewpoint can we encompass the whole history of zoology, and it is worth trying to get a series of different views of it. Only within the sciences is it appropriate to be satisfied with single explanations whereas in their history we must expect our findings to be additional.

Science, like most other human activities, is complex. We can look at its history under three broad aspects: as an intellectual, a practical and a social activity. It is science as an attempt to account for and categorise the booming, buzzing confusion of the world that has usually interested philosophers and historians; and especially since the nineteenth century, scientific methods and explanations have provided a paradigm for those working in intellectual fields remote from physics or biology. As an intellectual activity, science has had its history of relationships with other disciplines; and this is particularly true of zoology, as will become apparent from our study of illustrated books. For centuries animal pictures were chiefly important for their symbolic value, in association with a text reminiscent of Aesop's fables reminding the reader how to live; later they depicted the infinite wisdom and fecundity of the Creator; and finally became a convenient means of displaying the characteristics of an animal so that it could be properly classified. Zoology is thus revealed in its connections with a general world view, with theology, and with logic — as well as with aesthetic judgements. In zoological illustration, the mind guides both the eye and the hand.

Scientific theory is tested by experiment or systematic observation; and since Francis Bacon it has been expected that pure science, or 'experiments of light', will lead to applied science or 'experiments of fruit'. Both in the testing of theories and in its various applications to useful purposes, zoology like the other sciences is a practical activity. Zoological illustrations show the coming of the microscope in the seventeenth century, making possible experiment and observation that could not have been done before; and show too the economic value of zoology, in plates of improved domestic animals, and of wild creatures that would yield fur or oil, or merely a good meal for hungry sailors — who could also, by identifying sea birds, make a reasonable guess at how far they were from land.

Science is also a social activity. An isolated person could not get far in zoology or any other science, for these disciplines are based upon the idea of cumulative public knowledge. In the past often very informally, but since the early nineteenth century usually formally, men of science have had to learn

6

3
An improved hog, from
Holt's *Agriculture of Lancaster*
(1795)

their subject. In zoology, they very often took a medical degree if they were of
appropriate social position: for not only was this a training involving much
anatomy and physiology which would be valuable to any zoologist, but it was
also a passport into a profession, while particularly in the past there were not
many ways of earning a living as a zoologist. One might on the other hand
make scientific instruments, such as microscopes; one might under the patronage of an individual or a learned society go to distant places to collect
specimens; or one might earn a living as a zoological artist, as a painter,
engraver or lithographer — this being a career also open to women, although
fewer seem to have excelled in it than in botanical art.

Science is a social activity in that it is a career and we can see this aspect of
zoology again in illustrations. Since it is public knowledge, it is a social activity
in another sense too — it is essentially the product of a group or community.
Thus in the seventeenth century there came into being the formal scientific
societies — the Royal Society of London, and the Académie des Sciences in
Paris — which replaced the more informal and ephemeral groupings of the
Renaissance period, and have been imitated in other capitals since the 1660s.
These societies took under their wings the whole range of the sciences, and in
the journals which they published one finds papers on astronomy, chemistry,
botany, and zoology side by side. Such societies represented a nascent

8

scientific community, committed through discussion and publication to the cumulative advance of science; but it was still a very unspecialised community. By the end of the eighteenth century tensions and conflicts of interest between different groups of men of science were apparent, in what had become a rather larger scientific community; but in Britain in the opening years of the nineteenth century one still finds polymaths like James Parkinson writing on palaeontology and on the shaking palsy, J. C. Prichard on physiology, insanity, and anthropology, W. H. Wollaston on metallurgy, medicine, and the direction of the eyes in portraits, and Thomas Young on optics, chemistry, and Egyptian hieroglyphics.

Under the Presidencies of Sir Hans Sloane, who succeded Newton in 1727 and died in 1753, and of Sir Joseph Banks, whose reign extended from 1778 to 1820, the Royal Society became particularly oriented towards natural history; and the collections of these two men formed the nucleus of the British Museum's holdings in natural history. In Banks' time, exploration became the 'big science' of the day, requiring the support of government for voyages such as those of Cook, who was accompanied by natural historians and astronomers. Also during this period, in 1788, came the foundation of the Linnean Society, the first specialised scientific society in Britain, being dedicated to natural history; the collections made by Linnaeus had been bought by (Sir) James Smith, himself later the author of superb illustrated works of botany and zoology, who became the first President of the Linnean Society.

Meanwhile in France, the Museum at the Jardin des Plantes was becoming one of the great centres for zoology through the work done there on vertebrates and invertebrates by Cuvier and Lamarck. Museums of natural history were by no means a new idea; as early as 1655 Ole Worm of Leyden had published an illustrated description of his museum, which included many zoological exhibits. Bird-skinning was not generally practised until well into the eighteenth century, and the specimens of birds therefore still contained dried muscles which were sooner or later attacked by insects; but bones, fossils and shells were very durable. In 1681 Nehemiah Grew, the botanist, published an account of the Royal Society's museum; a very miscellaneous collection, including many zoological specimens which were duly illustrated. During the eighteenth century the cabinets of the curious were enriched with numerous curiosities from the three kingdoms of nature; but the best collections were often those in private hands, such as those of Linnaeus or Banks, or of Charles Willson Peale, who opened his museum in Philadelphia to the public in 1794. The Museum in Paris demonstrated the value of a great national collection; and such centres of learning gradually emerged in other great centres of science during the nineteenth century. These museums and collections duly produced their bulletins, journals or catalogues, appropriately illustrated.

While the systematic study of dead animals was going forward in the great museums — where in the tradition of Cuvier the fossil remains of extinct

9

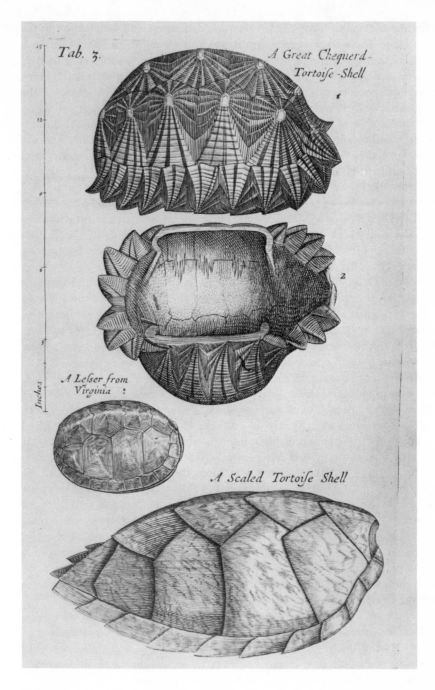

5   Tortoise shells, from Grew's *Musaeum* (1681)

animals, after due comparison with the bones and teeth of existing species, were being classified — exotic animals and birds were also being exhibited and studied alive in menageries. The great moving spirit behind the Zoological Society of London was Sir Stamford Raffles, the founder of Singapore, who on his return from the Far East in 1824 put enormous energy into the setting-up of the zoo in Regent's Park. Important people had for a long time kept exotic creatures in their parks; in the 1820s a Mr Wombwell had a travelling collection of animals which came to Oxford, where William Buckland, the Professor of Geology, was able to compare a living hyæna's way of crunching bones with what he had inferred to be the habits of an extinct hyæna. At Knowsley Hall, Lord Derby kept a menagerie; and when Edward Lear had published his magnificent studies of parrots done at the London zoo, he was duly invited to Knowsley to draw the animals there. Animals and birds drawn from life, rather than from stuffed skins, can be given a new vivacity and need not be depicted in unnatural attitudes. It was while he was at Knowsley that Lear began writing nonsense verse to entertain the children.

Illustrated works can therefore illuminate for us the social aspects of the history of zoology: the emergence of societies devoted to the science, the

6 Toucans going to sleep, from Bennett's *Zoological Society* (1830–31)

growth of museums, the sending out of expeditions, government support for the publication of the results of expeditions and private support for the publication of expensive fine books and also for cheaper works in bigger editions, and later the coming of formal courses in schools, colleges and universities. While therefore this is a book about books, it is also about the history of zoology in all its aspects — though by no means a complete history.

Anybody studying illustrated zoological works today may thus have in mind one or more of a whole range of interests. He may be concerned with the role of patronage in the eighteenth century, with what was known of the geographical distribution of animals at some time or other, with the sources used by some particular natural historian in whom he is interested, or with the history of engraving or lithography. For all these purposes illustrated works may be a useful source of information and answers, as well as giving pleasure to the less-earnest seeker after information who simply enjoys pictures of animals. It is only for this last group that the original artist will have had any great sympathy: one may draw with posterity in mind, but there can be few who have derived pleasure from the prospect that in due time their work may be used as a source for studying patronage or recovering some norm. The student of zoological illustrations, particularly historical ones, and the zoological artist have different purposes; and it is now time to turn to those of the artist, bearing in mind that these can in general only be determined from what we know of the state of the science in his day. Given this constraint, we can with some confidence decide what the purpose of the illustration was, and see how these purposes have changed over the years; bearing in mind that the artist, like the modern student of his work, may well have had more than one end in view — to depict an animal, to challenge some foreigner, and perhaps to demonstrate some new technique.

The primary purpose of any zoological illustration is to show what the animal is like; but that is more complicated than it appears, as we can see from the very different pictures of the same species that different artists have drawn, particularly when they have been working at very different periods in history. In the Renaissance, the task that faced the natural historian, whether in zoology or botany, was to depict creatures described in ancient texts. This might be a question of identifying a species of bird or animal, from a text which was unillustrated or where the illustrations had with successive copying become formal or unrecognisable. Here the problem was that the fauna and flora of northern Europe differ considerably from that of the Mediterranean region where the ancient texts had originated; and a devotion to the written word led to various rather implausible identifications of German or English animals and plants with Greek descriptions — as translated into Latin, after passing through Arabic and perhaps other languages too.

The problems were greater when creatures such as unicorns, chimæras, basilisks, and amphisbænas were described in the text, or cockatrices were

12

Black-Bird Cock Hen and Egg

7 Blackbirds, from Albin's *Singing Birds* (1759 edn)

8 Blackbird, from Yarrell's *British Birds* (1843)

mentioned in the Bible; that is, when the artist had to depict creatures that he had not seen, and had not come across anybody who had. In the sixteenth and early seventeenth century, this problem was not altogether different from that of drawing the camelopard (or giraffe); we know that these creatures do exist, while unicorns do not, but this was not clear to our ancestors who could after all buy unicorn's horn from the apothecary. In drawing exotic animals, the artist had to rely on his imagination, or on somebody else's in copying an existing picture.

Thus if we look at one of the earliest large-scale English books on animals, Edward Topsell's *History of Four-footed Beasts*, 1607, which was based upon Conrad Gesner's *Historia Animalium*, 1551–87, we find that it is a compilation, in alphabetical order, of the traditions concerning a whole range of animals. Topsell's preface makes it clear that this was a book intended for Sunday reading rather than for experts (had there been any) to use during their working day; its purpose was thus as much to edify and entertain as to instruct. Many of the creatures referred to were well-known to those who read the book; there are descriptions, for example, of asses, dogs, and horses, and these are illustrated from life, as are common wild animals such as the hedgehog. There is a good deal of farriery set down under 'Horse', which is altogether rather practical and down-to-earth until near the end where the sea-horse, or hippopotamus, is shown curiously treading water while crunching up a crocodile, and there is a casual reference to wild horses in India that have but one horn.

One would expect that as the author moved from familiar to unfamiliar species his descriptions would become rather less accurate, and that he would have a difficult time keeping a due balance between credulity and scepticism. To believe in the duck-billed platypus required some effort from the zoologists of 1800, and it has never been wise to suppose that we know the limits of nature's creativity. Among the exotic creatures Topsell described and illustrated was the Lamia, a formidable creature that would have been the despair of any taxonomist with its cloven hoofs on its back legs and claws on its front ones. Topsell admitted that some had affirmed that either there were no such Beasts at all, or else that it was a compounded monster of a Beast and a Fish' – but he added that such cavillers were ignorant. He thought that some stories of this creature were indeed old wives' tales, and others arose 'from the prestigious apparitions of Devils' anxious to deceive and beguile the minds of men. The Scriptures, on the other hand, did contain some descriptions of formidable monsters which Topsell concluded to be the Lamia; he therefore accepted the real existence of the animal, while denying that it could draw its victims towards its jaws by magic.

Similarly, Topsell believed in the unicorn, and in the Mantichore with its triple rows of teeth and its tail armed with sharp quills like that of a scorpion or porcupine. That he was not completely credulous in his use of the sources is shown in his account of the Hydra 'supposed to be killed by Hercules', for in

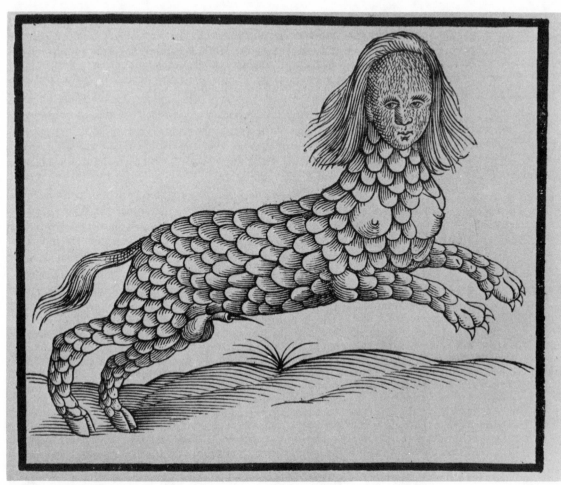

9 Lamia, from Topsell's *Four-footed Beasts* (1658 edn) — a tall story told in visual language

his second volume devoted to serpents he recognised this as something 'the poets do fain'. Nevertheless, he included a splendid illustration of this formidable creature, with seven heads and two front legs terribly clawed. There was a tradition of illustration of such monsters, and where Gesner, and after him Topsell, could find no drawing by an eye-witness of any animal they fell back on this common stock. Thus among the exotic creatures known to us to exist is the rhinoceros; here the illustration used was that of Dürer, whose magnificent armoured creature with an extra little horn on its shoulders, for centuries drove out more accurate representations of the rhinoceros.

In Topsell's day the rhinoceros was known for his supposed indomitable aggressiveness against his enemy the elephant and it was said that in the battle his resolve was always to conquer or die. To take the rhinoceros for one's

15

emblem, as some did at that time, was therefore to make it clear that one did not accept that discretion might be the better part of valour. Dürer's rhinoceros fits this conception better than a more accurate picture of the creature might; and this gives us a clue as to what was expected of zoological illustration in the Elizabethan period. Travellers intending to visit distant countries would not have made a point of perusing the pages of Topsell so as to know what fauna to expect. The book was designed for stay-at-homes, and while it gave a good idea of the appearance and habits of familiar creatures, when it came to treatment of exotics the object was to show what a recent author has called 'animals with human faces' — that is animals symbolising human characteristics.

We are familiar with the zoology of Aesop's fables, with their cunning foxes and crows; and with the 'generation of vipers' denounced in these terms by John the Baptist because young vipers were supposed to gnaw their way out of their mother's womb; and with heraldic animals generally. Down to the seventeenth century this was the chief value of the study of animals, and Topsell in calling his creatures Beasts may have been consciously putting himself in the tradition of bestiaries, in which this emphasis was all important. Such emphasis went with a world-view in which man the microcosm was a

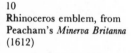

10
Rhinoceros emblem, from Peacham's *Minerva Britanna* (1612)

mirror of the great world or macrocosm, and in which everything was connected through a network of symbols and signatures. Not only zoology was interpreted in this man-centred way; chemistry was treated as alchemy, in which the purification of the alchemist's soul was as important as the transmutation of lead into gold.

In this symbolic science, the eagle stood for nobility, the lion for courage, and the grasshopper for improvidence. Once their essence was known, there was little need to study them further or to draw them more accurately than the accepted image, which after all called up the required associations. There was some need to study them, for early scientific man could not, as Adam had at first when he named the beasts, penetrate immediately to the essence and name them accordingly. The symbols might be variable, so that one animal could stand for more than one quality, and might change with time. Thus the butterfly, which began as a crawling thing, died into its crysalis-coffin, and rose again in glorious form, symbolised man in his earthly life, death, and resurrection; but with the passage of time it came also to stand for frivolity.

This interest in animals as emblems did not die out by the 1660s, but among men of science it must have become a conceit rather than a firmly-held belief — like the notion that there might have been something in alchemy. Thus Sir

11
Salamander in the fire, from Maier's *Atalanta Fugiens* (1617)

Humphry Davy in the 1820s studied Proteus, a curious rather newt-like creature in appearance, which lived in caves in Austria; nobody knew its origins, which were perhaps in some subterranean sea; it seemed capable of living both in air and in water, and was thus an amphibian, and it was thought that it might be an immature form of something higher. It was therefore an excellent symbol of the Great Amphibium, man, but while Davy made something of this in a literary dialogue, as President of the Royal Society and a contemporary of Cuvier, he can hardly have believed in it very seriously. But one should note that even in our own day, we expect that pictures of animals should be symbolically appropriate: if an eagle or a lion does not have an aristocratic expression, it does not look right, and in going subtly beyond naturalism an artist may produce a more satisfactory and convincing illustration.

This point can be subsumed under the general statement that the object of the zoological artist is to show us what the creature looks like so that we can recognise it. This statement can no doubt be accepted, despite our reservations about Topsell's Lamia and Mantichore, for if one did see one of these it probably would have to look like its picture in order to be identified. To do Topsell's kind of natural history required considerable erudition in reading and interpreting ancient texts and the Bible, and one might add that to describe and draw fabulous monsters requires erudition of no common kind. In 1646 there appeared Sir Thomas Browne's famous *Pseudoxia Epidemica*, exploding an enormous number of vulgar errors in natural history, and by the middle of the seventeenth century non-existent creatures were disappearing from zoological works.

In zoology the most important invention of the seventeenth century was the microscope, which revealed things never seen before; both new sorts of things, like spermatozoa, and new details of familiar things, like fleas. The illustration of things seen through microscopes rapidly reached a high point in Robert Hooke's celebrated *Micrographia* of 1665: he depicted specimens from the inorganic as well as the organic realm, but it was his zoological illustrations — of a greatly magnified fly, louse, and flea — which caught the imagination of his contemporaries. His was a low-powered instrument and the problem was to construct more powerful microscopes in which the image was not distorted beyond recognition. The poor quality of the image was in part due to the poor quality of optical glass in the seventeenth and eighteenth centuries, for it varied in density, and hence in refractive index, and there was little process control in seventeenth and eighteenth century industry to produce consistent results. Part of the problem too was that the microscope had overtaken optical theory, so that it was only in the nineteenth century that coloured fringes around the image were eliminated by the use of compound lenses, as had been done in telescopes (where it was easier) in the previous century. The compound microscope only then became a standard piece of equipment for the zoologist; on the official expedition under Captain Tuckey sent to explore the River Zaire in 1816 none of the natural historians dispatched under the aegis of the Royal Society could describe or draw specimens seen through a microscope, and subsequently even Charles Darwin relied on the simple microscope which was merely a powerful magnifying glass. The great botanist M. J. Schleiden described in his *Scientific Botany* of 1849 how to use a compound microscope and it was from about this date that the instrument came into general use, rapidly becoming much cheaper and better.

Zoological illustrators of earlier times therefore did not usually include microscopic detail unless they were drawing creatures only visible through a microscope — and that was relatively uncommon, except in those works devoted to insects where Hooke's lead was followed resulting in the beautiful illustrations of the eighteenth century. The problem encountered with Topsell, of drawing exotic creatures convincingly, was almost impossible to solve. The best answer was probably to draw it, or to get a native artist to do so, in its native country. Thus in the late seventeenth century Kaempfer got Japanese to illustrate animals of their country, while about a century later Mutis in Peru got local Indians to draw plants, and Reeves in Canton and Roxburgh at Calcutta similarly bought or commissioned natural history paintings, some of which were duly published while others simply remained in the archives of museums.

Artists in a very different tradition might not always show what zoologists wanted to see, though from numerous countries there have come exquisite paintings of easily-identifiable creatures. Otherwise, exotic animals were drawn from dead specimens and such pictures would be chiefly of value in helping one to recognise another dead one of the same species. We are apt to forget the toll which zoology has in the past exacted from the animal kingdom. The maxim was 'what is hit is history, and what is missed is mystery', and the successful 'collector' had to be a good shot; with any luck the bird or animal would provide his supper once it had been skinned, and remarks upon the flavour of creatures form a part of early field notes. Even in Europe the connection between field sports and natural history has always been very close: man in his capacity as hunter of grouse, trout, or fox has to learn a certain amount of the science if he is to be successful, and has sometimes gone on to learn much more than this.

Either the skin or the whole animal packed in spirits (in earlier times it would have been the eviscerated specimen) were sent home and then drawn by an artist. From the stuffed skin of an exotic bird, for example, it is very difficult to draw the creature as it would have looked alive. If the person who shot it made a sketch of it in a characteristic attitude — and in the days before photography an ability to sketch was much more common than it is today — then the artist could use that; but often he seems to have had little guidance, and could only pose the creature stiffly in what seemed a convincing (or at least

12 A shot specimen, from Gould's *Birds of Australia* (1848)

decorative) position on a standard mossy stump in his studio. Mammals usually look every bit as unconvincing as birds and were portrayed in very uncomfortable-looking poses (unless they were familiar to the artist, as they might have been if they were a species of fox or hare, for example, that could be drawn in an attitude like that taken by European species, though in fact they might comport themselves very differently).

There were two solutions to this problem. The first was to take the artist to the animal rather than the other way about. When Joseph Banks visited Labrador in 1766, he sent back specimens of birds to be painted by Peter Paillou and by Sydney Parkinson; they did indeed produce some very decorative pictures, but when he set sail with Cook in 1768 on the expedition that was to take them to New Zealand and on to Botany Bay, Banks took Parkinson along. Cook's later voyages also had an artist or two in the company, and the graphic records of expeditions from the later eighteenth century on are correspondingly rich both in landscapes and in natural history pictures. On the debit side were the risks of sea-voyages: the sailing-ship was probably the most dangerous means of transport ever devised, and Parkinson, for example, died on Cook's voyage from an illness picked up at Batavia in the East Indies. On

20

MACROCERCUS ARARAUNA.

Blue & Yellow Macaw

13   Macaw, from Lear's *Psittacidae* (1832)

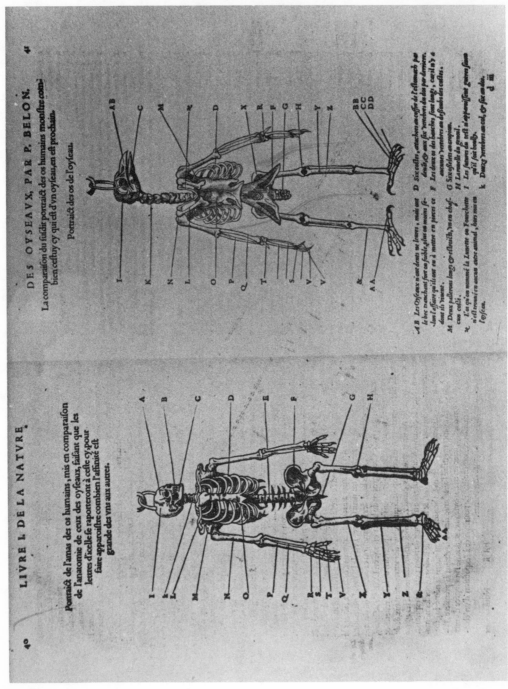

14 Homologies, from Belon's *Oiseaux* (1555)

22

the other hand, for the zoologist and the zoological artist to see animals in their diverse habitats was an experience not to be missed. It is no accident that many of the most distinguished natural historians of the eighteenth and nineteenth centuries learned much of their science on a voyage; those who did not, like John Edward Gray of the British Museum who turned down the opportunity to sail to the Pacific in 1823, came to suffer in reputation from their lack of field experience.

The second answer was to bring living exotic creatures to Europe, to some kind of menagerie or zoo. Edward Lear was one of the first artists to take advantage of this in his monograph on parrots — itself an early example of a picture book devoted to a single group of creatures — when he painted them in the London Zoo, and when he later painted birds and animals at Knowsley Hall. The disadvantage of this is that the creature cannot be shown in its natural habitat, and Lear's superb birds stand out against a very lightly indicated background. It is often said that Lear's birds have a particular character; that the picture represents an individual parrot or pigeon rather than an average or typical member of the species. It is one of the difficulties facing the zoological artist to decide whether he is painting Polly, or some member of a species of parrots; or rather to separate out what are the idiosyncracies of a particular specimen from what are typical. For the main object of the painting is to ensure that successors will be able to recognise the species, and not Polly herself — natural history painting is not portrait painting.

In one of his parrot plates Lear did indeed portray the feathers as they were disposed in his 'sitter', where they had happened to grow in an odd way — so in drawing an excellent portrait of this particular bird, Lear had produced a misleading illustration of the species. This is something that cannot be helped when an artist has only a single specimen to work from and this is partly why natural history collectors were so trigger-happy. To emphasise specific rather than individual characteristics, and yet to make the bird or animal depicted look alive, is very difficult; and there can be no doubt that Lear was one of the most successful artists in striking this balance in general. His relative absence of background does not in any way detract from the pictorial quality of his illustrations, though it does mean that they contain less zoological information than those which indicate habitat.

In painting animals or birds from skins, one can naturally only emphasise external characters. These are important for the description and recognition of the species, but they are not everything. For recognition, a lively picture of the creature in a characteristic attitude and habitat is valuable if the reader is to be enabled to identify living members of the species but for description the external characters may be far from fundamental. Aristotle had distinguished homologies (resemblances of structure which indicate closeness of relationship) from analogies (functional resemblances, like that between the wings of bees and birds, between organisms distant in the scale of nature). He saw the

23

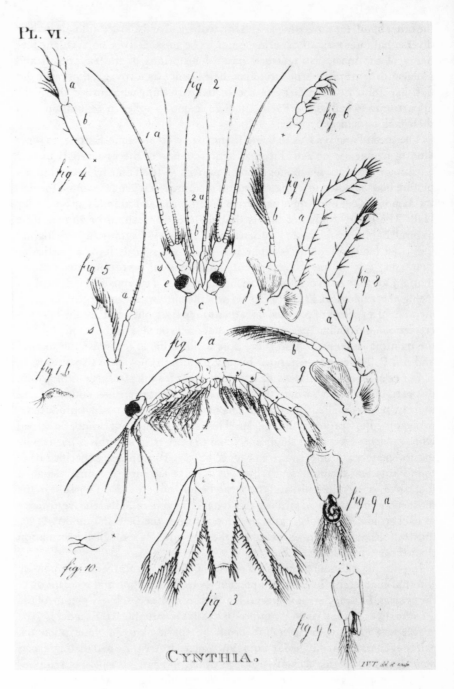

CYNTHIA.

15   A luminous crustacean, from Thompson's *Zoological Researches* (1828–34)

16   W. Curtis' *Brown-tail moth* (1782)

natural world as composed of natural groups of creatures sharing family resemblances, and believed that in classifying one should therefore weigh as many characteristics as possible of a species.

In modern times, the first naturalist to echo these Aristotelian emphases was Pierre Belon, whose book on birds appeared in Paris in 1555; the book not only illustrated birds eating their food, thus indicating habits and habitat, but also showed the skeleton of a man and a bird so as to bring out the homologies. A century later John Ray and his patron Francis Willughby, in handsomely-illustrated works, applied the Aristotelian concept of natural groups based upon a range of characters to both fishes and birds. Their classification was based upon dissection, and therefore on internal as much as external parts. In their work on birds, they remarked of Aldrovandi who had described a gannet from a picture only that 'Painters are not wont to be very exact either in expressing of the colours, or delineating the parts', yet their own book on fishes contained descriptions of 420 species of which apparently only 180 had been actually dissected by them. While by the early nineteenth century it had become the norm for fine botanical illustrations to include some sections of the flower, the canons of zoological art have never demanded the presence of anatomical details in a plate showing the outside of an animal; the effect is a greater realism in zoological than in botanical art, where the plant is as a rule depicted as though it were simultaneously in bud, in blossom, and in fruit. In Descartes' *De homine* some illustrations have flaps that lift up to reveal inner structures — but such complicated plates never became widely used.

Anatomical illustrations have therefore generally appeared separately from pictures of the complete animal; though plates can be found including both complete and dissected creatures, especially where — as in marine zoology — realism may seem relatively unimportant. Thus in Thompson's *Zoological Researches* of 1828–34 the creatures illustrated were minute and transparent; he investigated the larvae of crabs, and was the first to describe the extraordinary life-cycle of barnacles, which begin their lives as free-swimming shrimp-like creatures and only settle down in middle age. Particularly in depicting invertebrates, zoological artists often do illustrate the entire life-cycle in one plate, showing for example butterflies with their eggs, caterpillars, and chrysalises, although one would not see all these phases simultaneously; realism and zoological informativeness can be increased when, as is often the case, the caterpillars are shown on a plant which they eat, and sometimes even with a predator which eats them.

The classic case of a painter of animals who spent much time studying their anatomy is George Stubbs, whose *Anatomy of the Horse* was published in 1766; he spent weeks preparing the drawings in a lonely farmhouse in Lincolnshire, being apparently indifferent to the smell. With the rise of palaeontology in the late eighteenth century came the need to describe and indentify species from bones or shells alone. In such a case, any picture except an anatomical one can

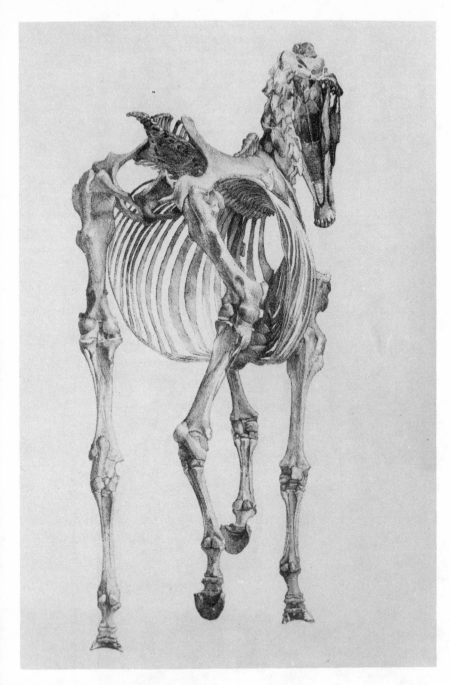

17   G. Stubbs' *Anatomy of the Horse* (1766)

18 Frontispiece to Mantell's *Wonders of Geology* (1864 edn)

only be an 'artist's impression' of more or less plausibility; thus John Martin, well known for his dizzying landscapes and illustrated guides to Hell, produced a splendid vision of those 'Dragons of the prime, that tare each other in their slime,' for the frontispiece to Mantell's *Wonders of Geology* (1838), but the serious illustrations in the text are of teeth and bones. One might have thought that such pictures must be instructive but repulsive, but this is not the case; the delicately washed or coloured illustrations for palaeontological books of the early nineteenth century are beautiful and do not immediately call up associations with the charnel house. This is especially true when they are depicting fossil invertebrates; the jaws of vertebrates, which were crucial for classification, do have less charm even when beautifully drawn. Palaeontological works sometimes show the fossils as discovered, giving therefore a realistic illustration of the mass of bones before the mind and hand of the scientist brought it back into order, if not like Ezekiel to life. The palaeontologist's reconstructions differ from anatomical drawings in that there is a certain degree of hypothesis involved in them; this element may be very small, as with a good fossil shell or a complete skeleton, or much greater as where a species has been based upon a single bone or tooth: like the cartographer, the illustrator should distinguish what has been actually observed from what has been inferred.

A useful technique in anatomical illustration is the exploded drawing in which the various parts are shown separated so that the structure and relationship of the parts and the whole can be clearly seen. This is particularly valuable in complicated structures, whether of fossil or living animals, and it is something that the artist can do and the photographer cannot. It is also a step further away from a picture of an animal in the direction of a diagram; diagrammatic illustration, in which everything not important for present purposes is omitted, is important in zoology, for example in showing how the

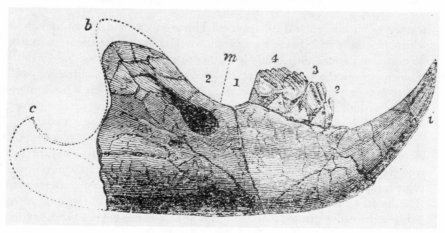

19
Jaw, conjecturally restored, from Owen's *Palaeontology* (1860)

29

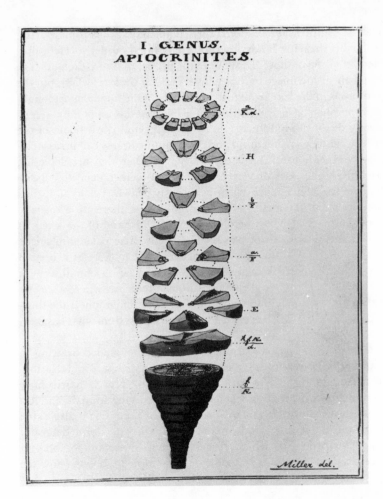

20
Exploded drawing, from
Miller's *Crinoidea* (1821)

feathers of birds in general are disposed. This is only an end of a continuum, of which the other end might be the Lear bird-paintings that are almost portraits; no drawn or painted illustration is ever a portrait as is a photograph, for in a zoological work the artist is trying to depict a species, and unobtrusively call attention to important characteristics of the species and divert it from unimportant or individual features. Importance is judged against contemporary schemes of classification and zoological theory, and therefore is variable.

Since the middle of the nineteenth century, photography has become increasingly important in zoological illustration, for in many ways it can record what the artist's eye cannot. Because the camera can catch movements of great rapidity, it can illustrate animal motion more accurately, in a series of stills, or in a moving picture; the classic case of this was the work of Muybridge, who demonstrated thereby that galloping horses never have their front legs and back legs splayed out as they were usually shown in hunting and racing prints. The camera can also be linked to a telescope or microscope, or even to an electron-microscope to reveal structures which are beyond the reach of the optical microscope, and can thus assist the study of behaviour of animals on the one hand, and of anatomy and physiology on the other. The cameraman is not in general a substitute for the artist, although he has taken over some of his functions: the two have a complementary role and the artist can still convey what an animal is like in ways that the photographer cannot match, and can tell us more about it in his picture.

The artist, in his efforts to show what a given creature looks like, has to make zoological judgements. Even when he is not directly displaying his anatomical knowledge, or lack of it, it will be apparent: Stubbs' horses always look right, for example, while Audubon, in his generally impressive attempts to bring drama into his pictures of birds, sometimes put them into anatomically-impossible positions — just as his predecessors had in posing the stuffed birds stiffly erect on a stump, though for opposite reasons. Much more often than not, Audubon's birds were caught by his pencil in an attitude they do adopt when alive, and it is this that makes him one of the greatest of bird-artists; the same is true, on a smaller scale, of his older contemporary Thomas Bewick, whose wood-engravings of the commoner British birds have never been surpassed and were done without the slaughter which Audubon found necessary for the production of his pictures. Bewick and Audubon as a rule showed only one species on a plate and in this they have been followed — as they were preceded – by many artists. But in order to fit more species on less pages, many artists have shown more than one on a plate and this has zoological advantages, as well as the disadvantage of devoting less space to each creature.

As a rule, when more than one species is illustrated, they are related or similar species: one plate may for example show a rook, a crow, a jackdaw, and a jay, another the different kinds of seal, or another the cartilaginous fishes. Such plates are found not only in formal works on natural history, but also in nineteenth-century encyclopedias, a very useful source too much neglected by historians of science and of illustration. Such plates are intended to be systematic. If we see pictures of a crow and a rook side by side, we shall see how they differ and recognise which bird it was that we saw in the garden; thus such plates can help the observer; while to the historian, they give information about the state of systems of classification. Species thought to be related, or close to each other in the chain of being in eighteenth-century terminology, are as a rule shown side by side, rather than those which appear similar being presented together. Mice and voles, or deer and antelope, usually appear on different plates, and only when there are a few species of a natural group found in one country might we find very different creatures put together — for example, the adder, grass snake, and slow worm might make one plate of British snakes, because that is all there are, and because it might be important

31

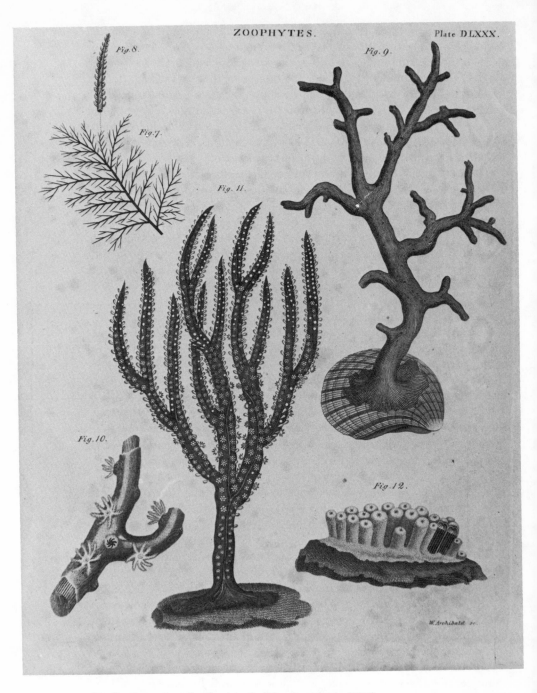

ZOOPHYTES.

Plate DLXXX.

Fig. 8.

Fig. 7.

Fig. 9.

Fig. 11.

Fig. 10.

Fig. 12.

W. Archibald sc.

21   Zoophytes, from the *Encyclopaedia Britannica*, 4th edn (1810)

to distinguish them in a hurry, although they are not closely related at all. Where related creatures are shown together, the illustration can complement the systematic part of the text, and it is interesting to see just which creatures are put side by side, in books of different periods.

A different principle, and one closer to nature from the artist's point of view, is to paint together creatures which are often seen together. This is an ecological rather than systematic approach to illustration; it is already being followed when creatures are shown on appropriate foliage, and against appropriate backgrounds of seashore, mountains, or forest. We do sometimes see closely-related species in close proximity, blackbirds and thrushes in the garden or Franklin's and California gulls following a plough for example, but as a rule we do not, and such additional information about their habitat and associations is not merely useful in itself but is another aid to identification. Illustrations may well still concentrate upon one great group of creatures; for example the shore birds of North America perhaps or the mammals of a British woodland might form the subject of one or more plates. In such geographical groupings, the roe deer would be shown with the fox and the badger and not with the red deer, which lives on moors. Illustrations of this kind might on the other hand include all the creatures that one might find in some situation, such as a rock pool. Such pictures bring out interactions between different species and emphasise the food-chains in the natural world thus producing a different, and more dynamic, zoological emphasis than do systematic illustrations. The picture can get out of control if too much background is shown, and too many creatures in it can look both implausible and bewildering; the zoological artist still has to select and emphasise what is important, and must not overload his picture.

Whether he shows one or more species on a plate, it is often useful for the artist to show the nest of a bird, with perhaps eggs and young; and to indicate whether the creature illustrated is gregarious or solitary, because one of the easiest things to observe is whether there are several of the animals together or only one. With gregarious birds this gives an opportunity of showing some standing or perching, and others in flight, which is very useful for identification. The range of variation in a species can also thus be indicated and it may therefore be worthwhile to draw several 'solitary' creatures together, though this is 'unnatural'. For identifying a dead bird (for example in a museum) an illustration which shows every feather is very valuable; but for a living bird a sketch, perhaps just a silhouette showing its outline against the sky when in flight, may be more important. In a sketch, the emphasis on showing only what is characteristic is carried further; perhaps the ideal is to have both finished plates and sketches in the same book, as has been some-times done — notably for example in Morris' *Birds of Prey of Australia*, 1975, and on a less sumptuous scale in Powers' *New Zealand Waders*.

What the zoological artist draws will thus depend upon the end he has in

22   Exotic bird and butterfly, from Edwards' *Uncommon Birds* (1747–51)

view. He may be drawing for systematists or for laymen, for an expensive or inexpensive work, and he may have many or few plates at his disposal. He may be illustrating a regional fauna, a particular collection, or a monograph on some genus, or perhaps doing a series of anatomical studies of one species. In any of these directions, he may achieve what ought to be his ambition, to produce works of art which shall be aesthetically as well as zoologically valuable. In any field one cannot please everybody, and what is perhaps astonishing is how successful zoological artists can be in satisfying those with interests that might be expected to be incompatible. Their works may survive removal from the text they were designed to complement, so that text and picture together defined and described the species; and we thus find zoological pictures being framed to go on the wall, or being reprinted with a new and usually less-interesting commentary, in rather muddier colours, reduced in size, and with all attributions deleted — as has recently happened to Gould's *Birds*, though his *Mammals of Australia* has received much more sensitive treatment and his *Birds of Australia* has appeared in a true, and naturally very expensive, facsimile. Even if illustrations do survive removal from their context, we learn much more from them in context, and should take context seriously. The context shows us some of the constraints under which the artist was working — he was working for a certain author and sort of book, for a certain publisher and public, at a certain price, and at a certain time; we should now turn to look at other constraints introduced when the drawing has to be printed in a book.

Bibliography

The lists following the first two chapters consist of general historical and bibliographical works. The illustrated zoological books are listed after the other three chapters, and under the authors in those lists can also be found recent bibliographies and editions of their works. The lists cannot be complete: no doubt many readers will find that owing to my ignorance or inadvertance, favourite works of theirs of great importance have been omitted — if so, I am sorry.

Two journals which are essential for anybody interested in illustrated works of natural history are the *Bulletin* of the British Museum (Natural History), *Historical Series*; and the *Journal* of the Society for the Bibliography of Natural History. Valuable general journals, covering all the history of science, include *Annals of Science*, the *British Journal for the History of Science*, *History of Science*, and *Isis* — which publishes each year a bibliography of books and papers in the history of science. Various reference works are very useful; such as the various national biographical dictionaries, and C. C. Gillispie (ed.), *Dictionary of Scientific Biography*, New York 1970–.

In the book lists, place of publication is London unless indicated otherwise.

Agassiz, L., *Bibliographia Zoologiae et Geologiae*, H. E. Strickland (ed.), 4 vols, 1848–54
Allen, D. E., *The Naturalist in Britain*, 1976
Anker, J., *Bird Books and Bird Art*, Copenhagen 1938
Archer, M., *Natural History Drawings in the India Office Library*, 1962

Blunt, W., *The Art of Botanical Illustration*, 1950

British Museum (Natural History), *Catalogue of the Library*, 5 vols, 1903–15; supplements, 3 vols, 1922–40;
  History of the Collections, 3 vols, 1904–12;
  Instructions for Collectors, 1902

Carus, J. V., *Geschichte der Zoologie*, Munich 1872

Cole, F. J., *A History of Comparative Anatomy*, 1949. Reprinted 1975

Dean, B., *A Bibliography of Fishes*, 3 vols, New York 1916–23

Dryander, J., *Catalogus Bibliothecae Historico-naturalis Josephi Banks*, 5 vols, 1796–1800

Eiseley, L., *Darwin's Century*, 1959

Engelmann, W., *Bibliotheca Historico-naturalis*, Leipzig 1846; Supplements, 2 vols, 1861; 5 vols, 1886–1907

George, W., *Animals and Maps*, 1969

Gillispie, C. C., *Genesis and Geology*, Cambridge, Mass. 1951

Gombrich, E. H., *Art and Illusion*, 1960

Gunther, A. E., *A Century of Zoology at the British Museum, 1815–1914*, 1975

Gunther, R. W. T., *Early Science in Oxford*, 14 vols, Oxford 1923–54;
  Early Science in Cambridge, Oxford 1937

Hagen, H. A., *Bibliotheca Entomologica*, 2 vols, Leipzig 1862–6

Henrey, B., *British Botanical and Horticultural Literature Before 1800*, 3 vols, Oxford 1976

Herrlinger, R., *History of Medical Illustration to 1600*, 1970

Honig, P. and Verdoon, F., *Science and Scientists in the Netherlands Indies*, New York 1945

Houghton, W. E. (ed.), *The Wellesley Index to Victorian Periodicals 1824–1900*, Toronto 1966–

Irwin, R., *British Bird Books*, 1951

Klingender, F. D., *Art and the Industrial Revolution*, A. Elton (ed.), 1968

Knight, D. M., *Natural Science Books in English*, 1972;
  Sources for the History of Science, 1975;
  The Nature of Science, 1977

Lewis, F., *Dictionary of British Bird Painters*, 1974

Linnean Society, *Catalogue of Printed Books and Pamphlets in the Library*, new edn., 1925

Lisney, A. A., *A Bibliography of British Lepidoptera, 1608–1799*, 1960

Lysaght, A. M., *The Book of Birds*, 1975

Merz, J. T., *A History of European Thought in the 19th century*, 4 vols, 1896–1914

Mode, H., *Fabulous Beasts and Demons*, 1975

Morton, L.T., *Garrison and Morton's Medical Bibliography*, 2nd edn, 1954

Mullens, W. H. and Swann, H. K., *A Bibliography of British Ornithology to 1912*, 1916–17

Mullens, W. H. and Jourdain, F. C. R., *A Geographical Bibliography of British Ornithology to 1918*, 1920

Nissen, C., *Die Illustriertern Vogelbücher Geschichte und Bibliographie*, Stuttgart 1953
  Die Zoologische Buchillustration, Stuttgart 1971–

Norelli, M. R., *American Wildlife Painting*, New York 1975

Pollard, A. W. and Redgrave, G. R., *A Short-title Catalogue . . . 1475–1640*, 1926

Raven, C. E., *English Naturalists from Neckham to Ray*, Cambridge 1947

Ritterbush, P., *Overtures to Biology*, New Haven 1964

Rowland, B., *Animals with Human Faces*, 1974

Royal Geographical Society, *Catalogue of the Library*, 1895

Royal Society, *Catalogue of Scientific Papers [1800–1900]*, 19 vols, 1867–1925

Rudwick, M., *The Meaning of Fossils*, 1972

Sherborn, C. D., *Index Animalium, 1758–1800*, Cambridge 1902

Sitwell, S., Buchanan, H. and Fisher, J., *Fine Bird Books, 1700–1900*, 1953

Strong, R. M., *A Bibliography of Birds*, 4 vols, Chicago 1939–59
Swainson, W., *Taxidermy, with the Biography of Zoologists*, [1840]
Swann, H. K., *A Dictionary of English and Folk-names of British Birds*, 1913
Taft, R., *Artists and Illustrators of the Old West*, New York 1953
Thornton, J. L. and Tully, R. J., *Scientific Books, Libraries, and Collectors*, 2nd edn, 1962
Vodges, A. W., *A Bibliography of Paleozoic Crustacea from 1698 to 1889*, Washington 1890
Vosmaer, G. C. J., *Bibliography of Sponges, 1551–1913*, Cambridge 1928
Whewell, W., *History of the Inductive Sciences*, 3 vols, 1837;
  Philosophy of the Inductive Sciences, 2 vols, 1840
White, T. H., *The Book of Beasts*, 1954
Wing, D., *A Short-title Catalogue of Books, 1641–1700*, New York 1945–51
Wood, C. A., *An Introduction to the Literature of Vertebrate Zoology*, Oxford 1931
Zimmer, J. T. , *Catalogue of the Edward E. Ayer Ornithological Library*, Chicago 1926
Zoological Society, *A Record of the Progress of the Zoological Society of London During the Nineteenth Century*, 1901

2

Techniques of
Zoological Illustration

All art is subject to constraints. These should not be seen simply as negative, for a work of art free from all constraint is as chimerical as a machine independent of all the laws of nature. An excellent machine, for example, fulfils its purposes within constraints imposed by the strength of materials and the sources of energy available, and is in general subject to conditions set out in the laws of mechanics and thermodynamics. Its efficiency is also, naturally, subject to the laws of economics, for one may not be able to afford what might be an ideal solution and one advantage may only be procurable at the expense of another. It has been remarked that really sympathetic and understanding men are unlikely to be very good at getting taxis and bullying head-waiters; similarly, it would be a mistake to expect Rolls-Royces, or folio works illustrated with nine-colour collotypes, to be cheap or available in tens of thousands.

Some constraints, like those imposed by the laws of thermodynamics, cannot be avoided; nobody designing a perpetual motion machine can expect success. In zoological art the equivalent of this would be the attempt to draw a golden eagle life size on a sheet of quarto paper. Other constraints are technical. In the nineteenth century it would have been impracticable to build an engine of aluminium, which was then a rare and expensive metal, whereas nowadays it is simply a matter of balancing its various advantages and disadvantages against those of steel. Just as the range of materials, and therefore the range of options, open to the engineer has widened down the centuries since the Renaissance, so the options open to the illustrator of zoological works have also increased. But having made his choice, the illustrator will find himself subject to constraints that place limits on his freedom and allow him therefore to produce works of art — which in his case must also be works of science.

We have already looked at the constraints imposed by the state of scientific theory and the canons of aesthetic taste; and we need do no more here than remind ourselves that if two people living far apart in time or place depict an animal differently this may well be because they have different ends in view. There is no one perfect way of drawing any animal, and two excellent pictures of the same creature may look very different — though the animal should in both cases be immediately recognisable from the picture. We do not therefore simply find progress in zoological illustration. Some of the best pictures have been done long ago; but we have different theoretical and practical interests, and more techniques for reproduction available to us. Indeed to approach the history of zoology through illustration, is a ready way of dropping the idea of science as cumulative progress to indubitable truth based upon some 'scientific method'. When we look at some system of beliefs and practices in Tibet or Fiji, we do not find it difficult nowadays to ask what function it plays in the culture of that society rather than whether it is true; and it is sometimes fruitful to look at the science of our own culture in the past — or the present — in the same light, and not as a series of 'discoveries' and 'contributions'. This view is even Darwinian in a sense, for evolution by natural selection does not lead inexorably to progress but to ceaseless adaptations to circumstances, and to both ups and downs.

In the West, down to the Renaissance there were no ways of printing illustrations — or indeed texts. The texts of works of ancient science, such as Artistotle's biological writings, or of medieval zoology, such as Frederick II's great work on hawking, had to be copied by hand. As we know today, even the most careful and expert typist or printer makes a few mistakes, and so it was with the texts; especially when like Aristotle's it had gone through several languages on its way to the west. But scholars have developed techniques for restoring texts since the Renaissance; while for illustrations the situation was a good deal worse.

One can see what happened from the various manuscripts of Frederick's book, where with each copying the birds have become more stylised and less recognisable. To copy pictures of animals is not easy, especially where the tradition is that animal pictures in manuscripts should be decorative rather than accurate; the features interesting to the zoologist, contemporary or later, are soon lost, and we have an animal picture instead of a zoological illustration. This can be seen dramatically in a series of the first illustrations of North American birds which have recently been published. John White made coloured pictures of the birds of Virginia at Raleigh's Roanoke colony in the 1580s. These were copied for Edward Topsell, who was planning to do a volume on birds as a companion to his books on four footed beasts and

39

serpents; the manuscript of this, *The Fowles of Heaven*, is the first work in which American birds were depicted in colour with a prose description, and Indian names. In T. P. Harrison's recent publication, these copies made for Topsell are printed beside different copies, perhaps by White's son, which had come down to Sir Hans Sloane; and it is striking and daunting how very different these two sets of copies, made at much the same time, are; the Topsell ones being generally less like the originals. Clearly, if zoology had had to depend upon copying by hand like this, illustrations would have been less valuable than they have in fact been for identifying species.

Even when methods of printing illustrations had been invented, colouring had still to be done by hand; and it was not until the latter part of the nineteenth century that colour printing became really practicable for zoological works. Many of the finest books of the first half of the twentieth century were hand coloured, for it is only in our day that printing has become better, as well as cheaper. Illustrated works of the past were often issued plain or coloured, so that if keen one could paint in one's own; this practice is said not to be extinct, so that not all the hand-coloured zoological works that one sees were necessarily painted in when they were new — the colouring may be very recent.

In 1971 a facsimile edition of Playfair and Günther's *Fishes of Zanzibar* (1866–77) was published, printed in the U.S.A. and with plates (only some of which were ever coloured) hand coloured in Formosa. The colouring is well done, but the book would not have met the more exacting standards of the nineteenth century because when painted the paper has puckered. Colour printing works better in our day. Hand colouring, even if it was not done by somebody who bought a plain set but was carried out under the publisher's supervision, was always a slightly chancy business. Painters differed in skill and in judgement of colours, and if one sees two copies of one of the great bird books of the nineteenth century side by side the colouring is generally rather different. Since colour in animals is variable anyway, these small variations are no bar to accurate diganostic use of the plates, and indeed may be held to increase their charm and interest.

Sometimes the differences in colouring may not have been originally so obvious, but have come about because the books have been differently treated — kept at different temperatures and humidities, or most important, exposed to different amounts of sunlight. Some of the pigments used were fugitive, and coloured illustrations should never be subjected to prolonged exposure to strong light. The first chemical study of pigments by a prominent scientist was the work of Sir Humphry Davy on the paintings from Roman ruins in Italy, and he wrote up his researches for the Royal Society's *Philosophical Transactions* (1815). The first synthetic dye, mauve, was prepared, and later produced in quantity, by W. H. Perkin in 1856, in the course of research at the Royal College of Chemistry in London on the synthesis of quinine; it is therefore a

23
Eel from Gunther and
Playfair, *Fishes of Zanzibar*
(1866–67)

splendid example of an 'accidental' discovery. It led to the establishment, chiefly in Germany as things turned out, of the synthetic dye industry; and to the general availability of fast dyes in a full range of colours. For the earlier part of our period, there is a study *Artists' Pigments, c. 1600–1835*, by R. D. Harley (London, 1970) which is a very valuable source of information on the nature and qualities of the various colours available before the coming of the synthetic aniline dyes. The availability of colours must have been a constraint upon zoological artists; but this is not evident, and the brilliant and sometimes even gaudy colours of eighteenth-century illustrations of birds and butterflies are most exciting. Artists and their colourists could achieve very splendid effects long before modern dyes came to their aid.

Small differences in colour are not usually very important in zoology, but there was hope in the eighteenth and nineteenth centuries that it would be possible to classify colours as it had been to classify plants and animals. Then without the expense and slight unreliability of coloured illustrations, one would be able to describe the colours of a specimen briefly and unambiguously. Such terms as one finds for example in ornithological descriptions, 'a rich fulvous brown', or 'an ash brown tint', or 'rich bay or chestnut red', convey a general but not an exact idea of what one is looking for. But just as by the end of the eighteenth century, it had become clear that animals could not all be placed on a linear system of classification — the Great Chain of Being, leading from amoebas up to men — so it turned out that the classification of colours was a more difficult task than had been imagined.

Newton's work on the spectrum, from the 1660s, had revealed that white light could be split up into rays of different colours, which on passing through a prism were refracted by different amounts. Rays of a certain refrangibility, a primary quality, aroused in us the sensation of a certain colour, a secondary quality; or so the phenomenon was described by Newtonian natural philosophers. In the nineteenth century, the wave theory of light, in the hands of Young and Fresnel, provided a further understanding of the situation, when refrangibility was interpreted as dependent on wavelength. But this is not enough to describe colour fully; as Goethe pointed out, the world of Newton's *Opticks* is a thin and idealised world, very different from the world in which we live. Colours differ in depth and brightness, and red things jump forward while blue ones recede; we cannot simply describe a colour as the effect on our retina of light of a certain wavelength.

The job of classifying colours was taken up by men of science working in very different fields. W. H. Wollaston, a crystallographer, in the early years of the nineteenth century noticed the dark lines in the solar spectrum now called after Fraunhofer, and interpreted them as natural frontiers between the different colours which otherwise seemed to shade into each other, but this curious idea led nowhere. In the mid eighteenth century Tobias Meyer, an astronomer upon whose lunar observations the *Nautical Almanac* was founded, had produced the first classification of colours in which a linear arrangement was abandoned; but his work again was of little direct use. Two contemporaries of Wollaston, Werner the great mineralogist and James Sowerby the first of a famous family of natural history illustrators, both proposed systems of colours because they were important in the taxonomic enterprises upon which they were engaged. But the problem was still too difficult, and it was not until near the end of the nineteenth century that a workable system of colour-classification was evolved by Ostwald, using a three-dimensional system of arrangement. But he was a physical chemist, and while his work has been taken up by paint manufacturers and in art schools it has not been greatly used by natural historians. Perhaps it is too exact; texture is as important as colour on an animal, and perhaps the 'ash brown tint' of the Victorian description is as accurate as it is possible to get, and beyond that one has to rely on a coloured picture rather than a precise description. Visual language many not be completely translateable into verbal language, or into mathematical language; which is why we still need illustrations at all.

We came to the hand-copying of colours from the hand-copying of illustrations generally; but the colouring we have been talking about presupposed a printed outline of the animal being illustrated. Printing came to Europe from

24
Animals, from *Aesop*, tr. W. Caxton (1484)

the east in the fifteenth century and some of the earliest printed books were illustrated with zoological woodcuts — at first these were illustrations for books of fables rather than of zoology in a strict sense. Woodcuts are cut on the plank of wood, that is with the grain running across them. The part that is to print black is left, and the parts that are to show white are cut away; so woodcut is a 'relief' process, like ordinary type, and woodcuts can appear on the same page as the type, being set up with it and printed in the same press.

Woodcuts are not as durable as type, but where long runs were required metal casts, called 'clichés', could be made from them by stamping the wood into an alloy of lead, tin, and antimony, at a temperature where it is soft but not molten, and will take up the fine details of the wood. This is a process similar to the 'stereotyping' used to prepare a cast of the type used for a book; both these technical terms have now come to be used chiefly in a metaphorical sense. Like most reproductive processes, printing from woodcuts reverses the original drawing; thus fishes are usually drawn facing to the left, but when printed are facing to the right. This reversal does not usually matter as much for zoological illustrations as it does for pictures of people where one is surprised to see them all apparently left-handed; but it does matter for anatomical drawings, and the

43

draughtsman preparing a drawing for printing should remember to reverse it so that the resulting illustration will look just like the original picture.

Clearly the degree of resemblance will depend upon the skill of the craftsman who transfers the original drawing in reverse onto the block, and cuts it. Some artists, notably Dürer, cut their own blocks, and we can in such cases accept that the printed illustration represents what the artist wanted — given that he really had command of the medium, and that the printing was satisfactorily done, for there are many factors in the production of printed pictures. After contemplating these hazards, we can rejoice that the Renaissance zoologists were so well served in their illustrations. In the great works of the sixteenth century, Aldrovandi's birds, and the numerous real and mythical animals in Gesner's books, are shown in splendid and lively drawings which often capture the characteristic attitudes of their subjects. Aldrovandi also

25
Nightingales in the nest, from Aldrovandi's *Ornithologia* (1645–52 edn); in this edition the plate was printed upside down!

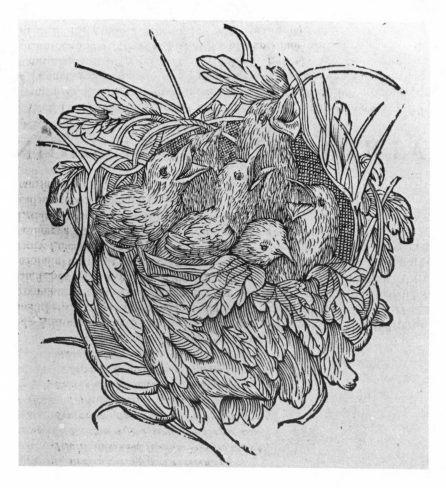

26
Plate from Willughby's
Historia Piscorum (1687),
done at Pepys' expense.

gave where he could a picture of the skeleton of a bird, and other anatomical illustrations, such as one of the oviduct of a hen; it is his work on birds which is most famous, but like his contemporaries Pierre Belon, Guillaume Rondelet, Ippolito Salviani, and Gesner, Aldrovandi was interested in the whole realm of natural history and was an indefatigable and encyclopedic compiler of information.

The greatest craftsmen could put an amazing amount of detail into their woodcuts; but there are limits to the fineness of the lines that can be printed by this method, especially when the cutting is not done by one of the greatest craftsman, as is often the case. This matters less for mammals and birds than for some other creatures, because there are not so many species of these to be distinguished and characteristic attitudes can be caught in a woodcut and be a great help in identification. But as the ichthyologist G. S. Myers has pointed out, in the reprint of Playfair and Günther, a fish is relatively rigid: 'He cannot sit down, stand up, run, turn his head about on a neck, scratch his ear, peck at his own foot, ruffle his fur or feathers, twist his body, or make many of the other movements with which most non-piscine vertebrates radically change their forms, outlines and external proportions from moment to moment.' One cannot therefore draw most fish in a characteristic attitude; though one can sometimes arrange them elegantly, as Willughby did in his *Historia Piscium*, one cannot get away with tricks.

There are indeed further constraints, for the exact positions of the fins and even of the scales must be plotted; there is no room for impressionism in illustrations of fish that are to be of taxonomic value. Woodcuts were not capable — except possibly in the hands of a master such as Dürer — of the accuracy and detail that was required. Pictures of fishes for the same reasons do not have the exciting naturalism of the best bird or mammal illustrations; the subject is clearly dead and no attempt is made to show it swimming under water, for this realism would be an obstacle to identification and so (as in a botanical drawing) enlarged parts, such as scales may well be drawn beside the fish. The illustration may well be aesthetically satisfying, and should be if it is well done; there is some small scope for differences of style as well as of accuracy, but in general fish illustration is a very formal branch of art, and the printing of such pictures requires a process capable of reproducing fine lines.

Much the same is true in the realm of conchology. Molluscs were classified

27
Grayling, from a dried specimen, from Franklin's *Journey* (1823)

Coregonus signifer (Back's Grayling)

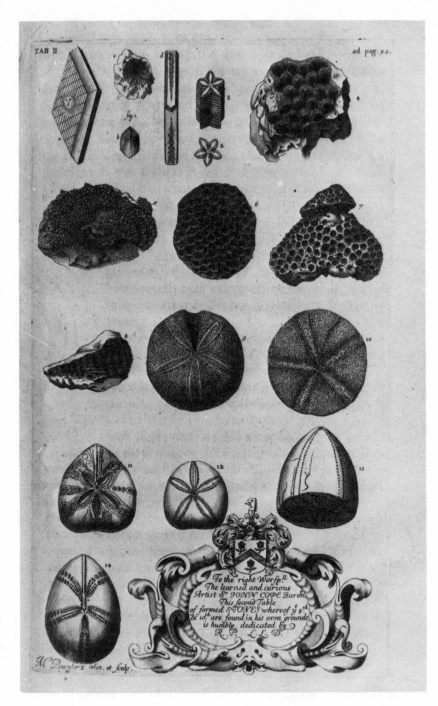

TAB II

To the right Worsp.^{ll}
The learned and curious
Artist Sr IOHN COPE Baron
This second Table
of formed STONES whereof y^e 9th
& 10th are found in his own grounds
is humbly dedicated by
R. P. LL. D.

M. Burgher's delin. et sculp.

28
Formed stones, from Plot's
Oxfordshire (1677): note the
dedication to a patron.

47

according to the form of their shells, with relatively little attention being paid to the creature inside (hence the name of the science), down to the nineteenth century. There are numerous species of shellfish and snails, and the forms of their shells do not differ very greatly; for taxonomic purposes, therefore, the illustrations must be very detailed and accurate. For spiral shells, it is clearly very important that the drawing is not accidently reversed, so that one with a right-handed screw appears as though it were left-handed (as happened in Buononi's *Ricreatione* (1681)); but in general, it is extremely important to show fine detail of the shells.

An advantage of classifying molluscs from their shells was that fossils could be brought into the scheme along with living species. Since fossilisation happens under water, there are far more fossils of creatures that lived in the sea or in rivers than on the land; fossil shells are thus the most obvious kind of fossils, and the most useful for characterising and dating strata. It was a long time before the real nature of fossil shells was put beyond doubt; indeed into the eighteenth century it was possible for reasonable men to argue that, like crystals or curiously shaped flints, fossil shells were the product of inorganic processes. Most were after all rather different from any existing shells in form, and they often differed in chemical composition; indeed very similar fossils might be found sometimes composed of calcareous matter (like real shells) and sometimes of flinty siliceous substance, and the chemists of the seventeenth and eighteenth centuries could give no very convincing account of how a shell could have been turned to flint.

Whatever one's belief about the nature of fossil shells, there was still the problem of classifying them: for like animals, they clearly fell into broad groups and were amenable to ordering or classification — that great object of the science of the Enlightenment. As Rudwick has demonstrated in his book *The Meaning of Fossils*, woodcuts were inadequate to the task of producing illustrations fine enough to serve for taxonomy in this field, as in ichthyology. We therefore find that even here with the first method of reproducing illustrations that was used, zoology was not monolithic; and now that choices of method are available, different solutions may be appropriate to solve apparently similar problems in different branches of the subject.

By the seventeenth century, taxonomy was becoming a more detailed affair, especially as new sorts of creatures were being reported by travellers in America, Africa, and Asia. The woodcuts which had made the reproduction of zoological illustrations possible only about a hundred years before were becoming a technical frontier, preventing the progress of taxonomy because illustrations could only contain a limited ˌmount of the detail required. The problem was solved with the use of engraved copper-plates; or occasionally for natural history illustrations, where a sharp line is usually needed, plates etched with acid — giving a softer effect.

In copperplate engraving the image is reversed as in woodcuts, the picture

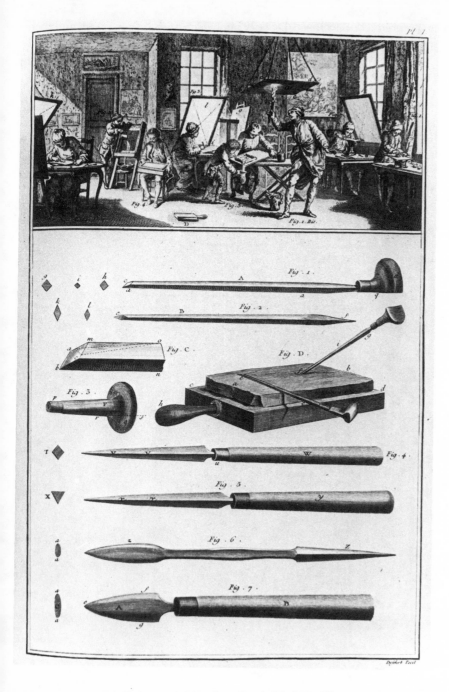

29 Engraving, from Diderot and d'Alembert, *Encyclopédie* (1751–80)

being reproduced on a sheet of copper into which lines are cut, inked, and then wiped so that the ink remains only in the depressions. The plate is then applied to the paper and what prints black is what was below the surface; engraving is an *intaglio* process and not a *relief* one. Engravings cannot therefore be printed on the same press as ordinary type, and only with a good deal of trouble can they be got on to the same page. This was in consequence very rarely done: and instead of the woodcut illustrations spread through the text, one finds copper-plate illustrations either grouped together at the back of the book or spread through the text but separate from the type. One advantage was that there was no temptation to the bad habit of putting text on the back of illustrations, where it inevitably shows through to a certain extent.

In fine illustrated books, where a page of illustration faced a page of text — often in the eighteenth century, a bilingual text — the system was both

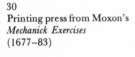

30
Printing press from Moxon's
Mechanick Exercises
(1677–83)

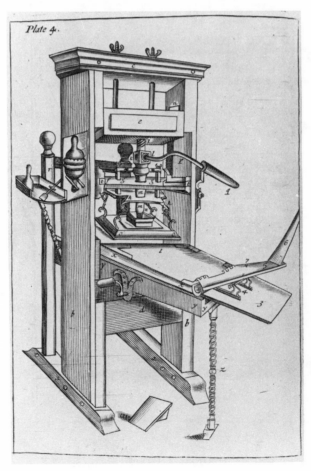

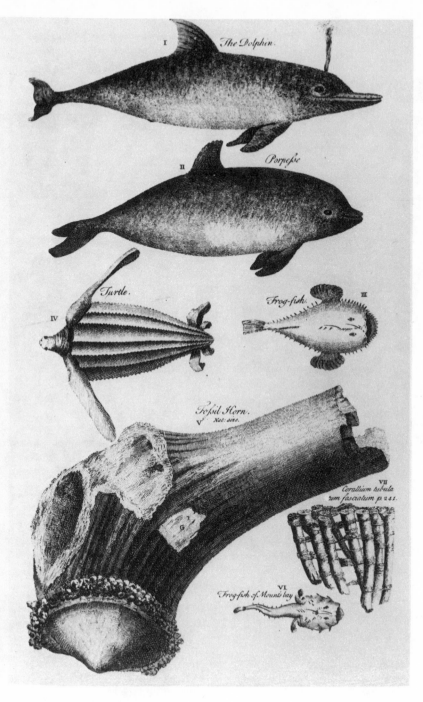

31
A miscellaneous plate, from
Borlase's *Cornwall* (1758)

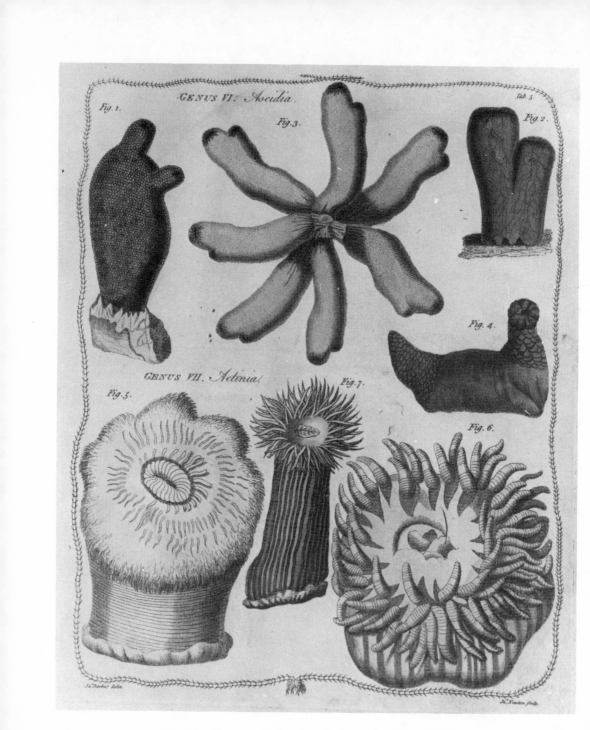

32 A prettily arranged plate, from Barbut's *Genera Vermes* (1783)

splendid in effect and very clear. For less expensive works, it is annoying that one has to flip over the pages to find the relevant illustration, which will often contain irrelevant detail, be not very clearly numbered, and be grouped so as to get as much on the page as possible rather than to produce a satisfactory-looking sheet. The best engravers did however become skilful at placing their various pictures on the page. Where the subjects are meant to be compared — to display homologies perhaps — then to have several pictures on one plate is of course helpful; it is the miscellaneous groupings which are tiresome.

As in woodcut, so in engraving, a craftsman came between the artist and the printed illustration. Some of the finest work was done when the naturalist was his own artist and etcher or engraver: as for example Mark Catesby had to be for his superb *Natural History of Carolina*, for he could not afford to pay for the engraving to be done by somebody else, and did the etching himself. A good engraver on the other hand would work up a pretty rough sketch made by a natural historian into a finished composition, much more accomplished but perhaps duller than the original. We should remember in these days when most of us feel all thumbs on being faced with a pencil and a sheet of paper, that an ability to sketch was expected of, and was tolerably uniformly distributed among, those who had had some education; the invention of the photographic camera has diminished that particular skill. An engraver would have been trained to work up such sketches; and if he was knowledgeable about science too, as were for example those who regularly worked for the Royal Society's *Philosophical Transactions* or for publishers of natural history books, the results could be extremely good. The detail that can be shown on copper is very fine indeed, particularly given a range of engraving tools; and a skilled engraver could readily indicate the various textures of the animals, or parts, that were being illustrated. Until well into the nineteenth century, engraving on copper was the best way of printing illustrations and it was used even for enormous works such as Audubon's *Birds of America*.

The very fine detail of copperplate engraving can only be exploited to the full if it is printed on excellent paper. The quality of the paper shows itself in two ways: it should be physically consistent, free from lumps, and with a good surface for taking the ink, and its chemical composition should be such that it will not with the passage of time become brittle, or readily show the brown stains of 'foxing'. The best paper has always been made from rags, and down to the nineteenth century was made by hand; in this as in other industries, there was little quality control based upon science, but excellent paper was available right through our period. The problem was to find paper appropriate for the text and illustrations, which might well have different requirements; at the mills the paper was made by traditional rules of thumb.

Sometimes, even when money was no object, a paper was chosen which has become liable to foxing; anyone who regularly scans booksellers' catalogues will be familiar with entries such as 'this copy shows some of the foxing which

33 Ivory-billed woodpecker, from Catesby's *Carolina* (1731–43)

54

always seems to be found in this book, but few illustrations are badly affected'. In the field of botanical illustration, Bateman's very splendid enormous folio on the orchids of Mexico and Guatemala (1837–41) is an example of the type. But as a rule, the more expensive the paper the better it has lasted. One can see this if one compares two contemporary journals, an expensive and a relatively cheap one; for example the Royal Society's *Philosophical Transactions* and Thomas Thomson's *Annals of Philosophy* in the second decade of the nineteenth century.

Thomson was a chemist, and ultimately became a professor of chemistry at Glasgow; and *Annals* therefore included a large number of chemical papers, some of them very important. But it was a general journal, and as a result contained a great deal of natural history (especially geology), some of it reprinted or translated from other publications. Its format was octavo and its typeface small; the paper is rather thin, and has gone brownish in 160 years, and the type shows through a little whilst the plates have offset onto the facing pages of text. Thus while the journal is very valuable for anybody wanting to understand the state of science in the early nineteenth century, it is not now, and never really was, an object for aesthetic contemplation.

The *Philosophical Transactions*, which had begun in the 1660s on a plan not unlike that of *Annals*, had by the Regency become a handsome large quarto publication, beautifully printed on excellent paper, and lavishly illustrated where necessary. Such a production was expensive; the cost of the illustrations was a point upon which Charles Babbage seized in his famous polemic of 1830, *On the Decline of Science in England*. Babbage was a professor of mathematics and the inventor of a calculating machine which was a clockwork-driven forerunner of our computers; thus by 'science' he meant 'physical science' which he felt was being neglected in comparison with the money and attention put into the life and earth sciences.

He remarked that 'Previous to 1810, there are upwards of seventy plates to papers of Sir E. Home's [on comparative anatomy and physiology]; in many of these . . . the workmanship is not so minute as in the succeeding ones. Since 1810, there have occurred 187 plates attached to papers of the same author. Many of these have cost from twelve to twenty guineas each plate; but I shall take five pounds as the average cost of the first portion, and twelve as that of the latter. This would produce,

$$70 \times 5 = 350$$
$$187 \times 12 = \underline{2244}$$
$$£2594.'$$

Babbage thought that one might be permitted to doubt whether such a large sum might not have been more beneficially spent in a different way. He also protested about the printing of Davy's Presidential *Discourses*, published in 1827 in a format such that it could be bound up with the *Philosophical Transactions*; and this gives us an idea of other costs. Davy's was an unillustrated

55

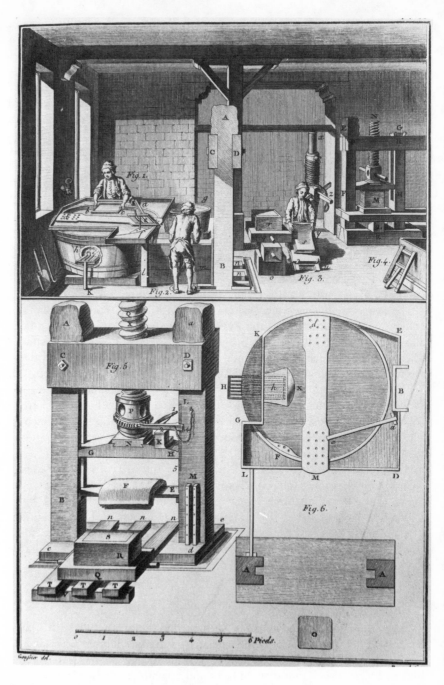

34 Papermaking, from Diderot and d'Alembert, *Encyclopédie* (1751–80)

1. Flat Fish
...in a Stratum
...Limestone.

W.R.C.De

35
Fossil fish, from *Annals of Philosophy*, 6 (1815)

volume of 160 pages, and the cost of 500 copies was £150, being £60 for twenty reams of paper, £60 for composing and printing, and £30 for alterations. The Society bought them at a trade price of fifteen shillings and three pence each. In 1818, for example, the *Transactions* contained 560 pages, and twenty-three plates; such a volume would therefore have been beyond the means of those who subscribed to Thomson's *Annals*, who had to put up with less minute workmanship than their more affluent contemporaries in the Royal Society.

Babbage also complained that the Society had lent Home all the copper plates to be used for illustrations for his large work on comparative anatomy; the book was thus extensively subsidised, in effect, by the Society. In this case, as Babbage put it, 'it might have been as well not to have obliterated from each plate all indication of the source to which he was indebted for them'; but usually those who did borrow their plates to use elsewhere were more honest than this, and such indirect subsidy was valuable. The Society in Babbage's day had about 700 members, of whom about 100 had actually contributed one or more scientific papers to its *Transactions*; the others were gentlemen of some position, interested in the sciences, who were thus helping to diffuse knowledge not only among themselves (for they, and various libraries, alone recived the *Philosophical Transactions*) but also later among those who bought books written

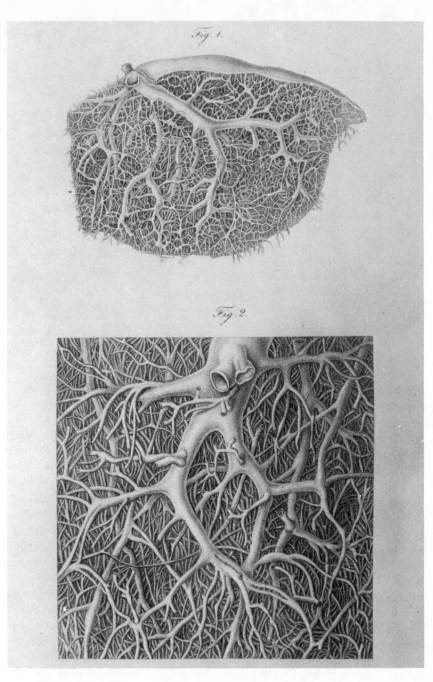

36 Dissections of the spleen, illustrating a paper by Home, *Phil Trans, 111* (1821)

by the Fellows and illustrated with plates used in its publications. Babbage indeed noted that 'the Society is not in a state approaching to poverty.'

If an illustrated scientific work were not directly or indirectly subsidised by the opulent, it might be supported by the government. Thus just at the time when Babbage was writing, [Sir] John Richardson was bringing out his *Fauna Boreali-Americana*, describing the zoological specimens collected on the expeditions in search of the North-West Passage under Sir John Franklin and Sir Edward Parry. These were official expeditions; and Richardson succeeded in obtaining a grant from the Treasury of a thousand pounds 'to be applied solely towards defraying the expense of the engravings', half of which had been devoted to the birds and mammals, and the rest to fishes, insects, and plants. In the former parts, there were seventy-eight plates; if these cost £500, that comes to rather over £6 each, and since the fifty bird plates were coloured (unlike plates in the *Philosophical Transactions*) Richardson's claim that 'rigid economy' had been practiced seems justified. The plates were well done, the birds by William Swainson and the mammals by Thomas Landseer; but the detail required was less than in the anatomical plates of Home.

Richardson's volumes were published by John Murray, as Davy's *Discourses* had been; and later scientific works of a similar kind, for which grants were similarly made available, were also published commercially. Thus Beechey wrote in his account of his voyage into the northern Pacific in 1825–8, published 1831, that 'notwithstanding the liberal assistance of his Majesty's government, there is so little encouragement for works of the above-mentioned description, that they could not be published unless the contributions were gratuitously offered to the publishers.' Two decades later, the American government itself published the Pacific Railroad Reports in a sumptuous edition, as an official publication. The natural history portions of these twelve volumes are handsomely illustrated, but although they look attractive enough to the uninitiated, the fish — for which particular care is required — were not very well done and the printed plates show considerable falling away from the original drawings by J. H. Richard, which are in the Smithsonian; apparently the job had gone to the lowest bidder.

In 1881, when one might have supposed that illustrations were rather less important than they had been half a century earlier, as the life sciences became more laboratory-based, J. W. Dawson remarked in his Presidential Address to the Royal Society of Canada, that 'the Canadian naturalist is often obliged to be content with the publication of his work in an inferior style and poorly illustrated, so that it has an aspect of inferiority to work really no better, which in the United States or the mother country has the benefit of sumptuous publication and illustration. On this account he has often the added mortification of finding his work overlooked or neglected.' By this time the *Reports* of the *Challenger* expedition were being written up (in fifty tomes altogether) under British government patronage; it is those for whom 'science' means

37
Fish, from the *Pacific Railroad Reports*, VI (1855)

'physics' who are apt to underrate the support for science given by governments in the nineteenth century.

One of those who benefited from having his work published in the *Philosophical Transactions* because he could then use the plates again in a book, was William Buckland, whose *Reliquiae Diluvianae* came out in 1823. In the book, and the earlier paper, Buckland described bones found in the Kirkdale Cavern in Yorkshire, those of hyænas being particularly noteworthy. After writing the paper, he assembled more evidence about Kirkdale and about other caverns, interpreting all this material as proving correct the Biblical account of the Flood; and to present this new evidence he needed new illustrations. To get plates engraved was so expensive that for the new pictures he used the new process of lithography which, being relatively cheap and sometimes also particularly suitable, had by the second half of the nineteenth century come to displace engravings on copper as the medium for most of the best work in

60

natural history. Their cost was about one third that of engravings; in geology this was especially important, because it meant that far more maps, sections and illustrations could be published.

Lithography was new in that it was neither a relief nor an intaglio process. A picture was drawn with a greasy crayon on the stone which was then wetted; when it was inked with a greasy ink, the ink would only adhere to those parts of the stone that had been marked by the crayon, and the picture could therefore be printed. It is difficult to get the fine details on a lithograph that could be achieved on an engraving on copper, and some lithographed anatomical drawings are fuzzy; for example, J. V. Thompson's *Zoological Researches* on marine invertebrates (1828–34) were illustrated with copperplates engraved by the author, except for the last one (No. VI of part 5) which is a rather smudgy lithograph.

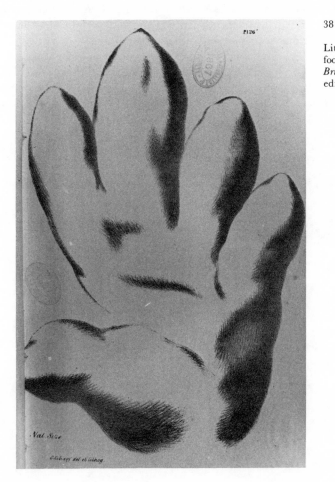

38

Lithograph of a fossil footprint, from Buckland's *Bridgewater Treatise* (1837 edn)

On the other hand, lithography was well adapted to showing light and shade, and was particularly suitable for large illustrations because the line was made with a crayon pulled across the stone, rather than with a burin pushed across the copper, and therefore looks more easy and flowing. In Buckland's book, the lithographed plates compare well with the engraved ones; but unlike Thompson, Buckland had employed an artist, G. Scharf, to draw the bones on the stone, and had the plates printed by Hullmandel, the leading lithographic printer of the day. This indicates that one of the apparently great advantages of lithography (elimination of the craftsman who stood between the artist and the published illustration) was to some extent illusory. Some artists did indeed draw their specimens directly on the stone; but many continued to prepare a drawing which was then transferred (reversed) to the stone by somebody else.

Lithography might have lent itself to colour printing, as woodcut might have done; that is, colour printing in these media would have been possible in the early nineteenth century, the period of the great Japanese coloured prints. Hand-colouring with all its possibilities of vagary was nevertheless superior to any economical printing process available for works of natural history; and when towards the end of the nineteenth century chromolithography came into use the effects were all too often unattractive and crude, and always a little

39
Lithography, from
Hullmandel's *Art of Drawing
on Stone* (1824)

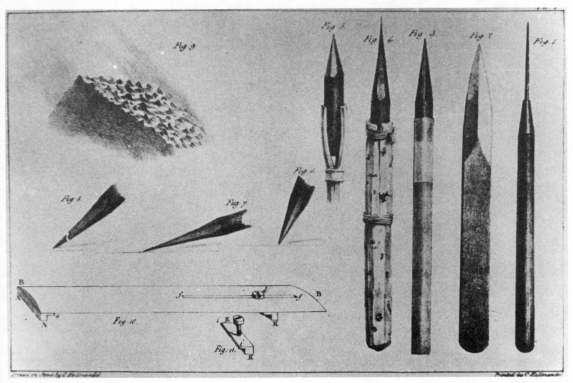

40
Fox, from Bewick's
Quadrupeds (1790)

muddy. Audebert's birds had earlier been printed by a secret process, producing splendid metallic tones, but were not cheap.

Lithography was invented in the very last years of the eighteenth century, just when the woodcut was being given a new lease of life by Thomas Bewick. Where the old woodcuts had been cut on the plank, he used the end grain of boxwood, which is very hard, and tools similar to those used for engraving copper. This process is therefore called wood engraving. Like the old woodcuts, Bewick's pictures could be mounted with the text; the blocks are extremely durable and very long print runs indeed have been printed from some of them. Fine detail can be shown and Bewick's pictures of birds and of quadrupeds are justly famous, as are his little tailpieces which became a feature of many nineteenth-century books.

For inexpensive works the woodcut became the standard means of printing illustrations, bringing the pictures therefore back onto the page, and making illustrated books more convenient to use than they had been in the eighteenth century. Boxwood comes from a small tree, and therefore one cannot do large illustrations by this method unless, as was done for illustrated Victorian magazines, the picture is printed from a number of blocks mounted side by side. For scientific illustration, the process was used for small pictures in the text; but later in the century it was sometimes used to print illustrations, often very detailed, based upon photographs. But whilst its ideals came closer to

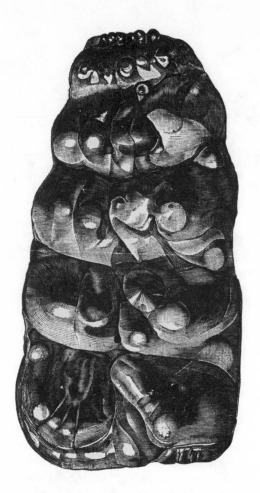

41
Mastodon tooth, from
Lydekker's *Life and Rock*
(1894); the horizontal line
from where the two blocks
joined is just visible.

those of photography, it was doomed by the invention of direct methods for
making blocks from photographs, and it only survived for diagrammatic
illustrations.

Like Dürer, Bewick cut his own blocks from his own drawings; although he
was no great naturalist his birds and animals show evidence of very careful
observation. Naturally there were very few men of science who could cut a
woodblock, something which is clearly much more difficut than drawing with
a crayon on stone. Therefore those who wished to prepare their illustrations to
their own exact requirements tended to use lithography. However since lithographs need to be set on a different press from type (unlike the more versatile
woodcut), the advantage of mounting illustrations on the same page would be
lost. Because woodcuts were small, and could show a great quantity of detail
and even light and shade, they were not meant to be coloured, though no doubt

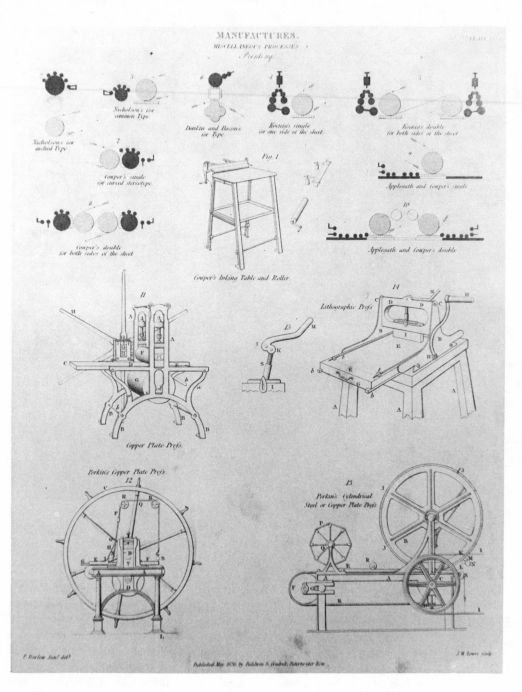

42   Lithographic and copper-plate presses, *Encyclopedia Metropolitana* (1817–45)

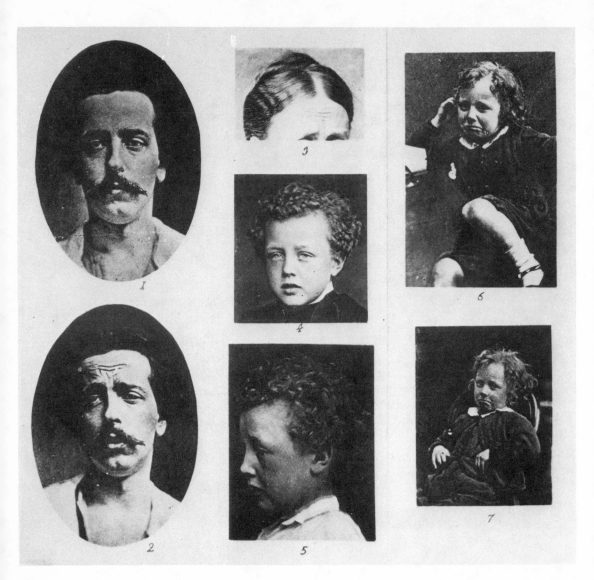

43
Photograph, from Darwin's
Expression of Emotions (1872)

sometimes those who bought books thus illustrated did paint them themselves. Colour printing from woodcuts for natural history never really established itself in the west. In general the medium limits picture size to less than an ordinary octavo page, so the principle that one should depict creatures life-size — which lay behind the enormous volumes of the nineteenth century — could not as a rule be applied in books illustrated by woodcuts.

Photography was introduced rather slowly in zoological illustration, and still in books describing some expedition or embassy in the second half of the nineteenth century, we usually find that whilst various landscapes, trees, and street scenes are worked up from photographs, the animals are illustrated from drawings. The chief reason for this was that cameras were cumbersome and required long exposures, and could therefore only be applied to exceedingly tame creatures. An early work illustrated by photography was Darwin's *Expression of the Emotions in Man and Animals* (1872), but only the human subjects were photographed, the animals being drawn from life and engraved on wood. Ewart's elegant little work on the *Pennycuik Experiments*, 1899, on cross-breeding of zebras and horses, and on reversion, does contain photographs of the animals studied.

By the end of the century it was possible to take fast exposures, and thus to catch with the camera movements which were too rapid to be followed by eye, the classic example being Muybridge's celebrated studies of humans and animals in motion in the 1880s which cleared up the question of just how horses gallop. Alfred Newton's invaluable *Dictionary of Birds* (1893–6) has a photograph illustrating the trajectory of a bird's wing in flight, which again, because of its rapidity, was not revealed by the naked eye. But for the bulk of his illustrations Newton used woodcuts after drawings from various artists, notably Swainson.

A difficulty about photographs of animals is that they can only show a particular individual at a particular time. Photographs of transparent or beautifully-camouflaged creatures are unlikely to be very helpful, unless the point is to show how hard they are to see in their environment, rather than to show what they look like. Any individual differs from the norm, and while an

44
Trajectory of a crow's wing, from Newton's *Dictionary* (1893–97)

artist, if he is experienced and knowledgeable, can make allowance for this and play down individual variations, or show two specimens indicating the range of variability, the photographer cannot. Photographs may thus be much less clear than drawings; they may give much less information about allied species or habitat; and they cannot emphasise 'important' characteristics at the expense of unimportant or purely individual ones. They cannot therefore replace zoological illustrations prepared from drawings for all purposes.

There are some occasions where it is an advantage that one is seeing an individual animal rather than a type specimen, and in these cases photography is ideal; especially where one wants to catch the animal in various movements that cannot easily (or at all) be followed by the eye. An excellent recent example of this is the work of G. L. Flanagan and S. Morris in *Window into a Nest* (1975); a study of the meeting and mating of two individual bluetits, their making a nest, laying eggs, and raising a brood. Here we have moved away, as it were, from the average bluetit, just as photographs get us away from the abstraction of the average man; and we see how individual bluetits behave at the most dramatic points of their life cycle. Such a work requires not only technical virtuosity of its authors, but also theoretical background; the Darwinian theory gave emphasis to individual variation, to the survival value that must (in a world where only the fittest survive) lie behind any patterns of behaviour, and to the balance of nature. Even had the camera been invented 200 years ago a naturalist like Gilbert White, for instance, would have been unlikely to have taken these photographs because he would have been asking rather different questions. No observations can escape some theory-loading, whether it is an artist or a photographer who is choosing what to portray. A series of photographs can help anybody doing a zoological illustration, rather as a number of specimens can, by showing a range of variations and attitudes, and thus allowing him to escape from the individual portrait.

The ordinary photograph in black and white was followed in our century by the coloured photograph, which can be used to achieve splendid effects, but falls short of painting both in accuracy of colours and in indicating textures. Bird photographs do not bring out the metallic tints and the contrast of glossy and matt surfaces on the feathers, for example; and if one compares the different colour photographs of the same birds in *Window into a Nest*, for example, one notices that the colours are inconsistent, although not displeasing. Every photographer knows how different conditions of light, and different batches of film, do bring distortions in colour photographs; and this fact is no problem, in holiday snapshots or in zoological illustration, unless one supposes that the camera cannot lie.

Through spectroscopy, photography since the 1860s had been used to cast light upon the structure of matter, and even the composition of the stars. At the end of 1895, Röntgen discovered x-rays, which could bring to light the structures of living things; and a photograph of the bones of his hand was one of the first demonstrations of the effect. Because on the whole it is easier to do our anatomy on the bones of dead creatures, rather than from x-ray photographs of those of the living, this discovery proved much more valuable in medicine than in the field of zoological illustration; everybody knew already where the bones went. But x-rays did have their value in physiological studies, which could be illustrated with x-ray photographs.

Spectroscopists had found it convenient to photograph spectra, and then to study the spectrum at leisure and in more comfort than can be achieved by bending over the spectroscope. For the faint spectra of stars, it was photography that made possible the identification of the otherwise imperceptible lines that indicate the presence of the various chemical elements. Photographs could also be taken through microscopes; but in that case they were merely recording mechanically, and perhaps less clearly, what the trained observer could see and draw.

In his famous anonymous *Diary of a Naturalist* (1829), Knapp wrote: 'were the powers of vision so enlarged or cleared as to bring to observation the now unknown fabrication of animate and inanimate things, what astonishment would be elicited.' x-rays were one such enlargement; but more significant in zoology were beams of electrons. In 1897 J. J. Thomson investigated such a beam, and concluded that it was composed of small corpuscles; but in the twentieth century electrons were shown to have a wave aspect too, so that they could be diffracted and focussed rather as light waves can be. The importance of this discovery was that there is a limit to the resolving power of optical microscopes, set by the wavelength of light; magnifications of much over one thousand times are impracticable. Just as x-rays allowed one to penetrate below the surface, and work out first anatomical structures and then the positions of atoms in crystals, so electron diffraction offered the chance of resolving structures much too small to be clearly seen by even the best optical microscopes – which by about 1900 were approaching their limit. In the electron microscope, where the beam is photographed or where its image on a special screen can be viewed through an optical microscope, magnifications of hundreds of thousands are possible. The structures of nerves and muscles can be seen, and individual large molecules are made visible; but the interpretation of what one is seeing is not easy, and usually a photograph is taken and studied at leisure.

Zoological observation, and in its train zoological illustration, had therefore passed from the magnification of what could be seen with the naked eye down to what could previously only have been inferred. In x-ray and electron microscope photographs, the camera is recording what otherwise could not be seen; and in zoological works nowadays, the photomicrograph taken through an electron microscope is often to be found, illustrating the fine structure of some part of an animal or bird.

In books of the nineteenth and early twentieth centuries, photographs were

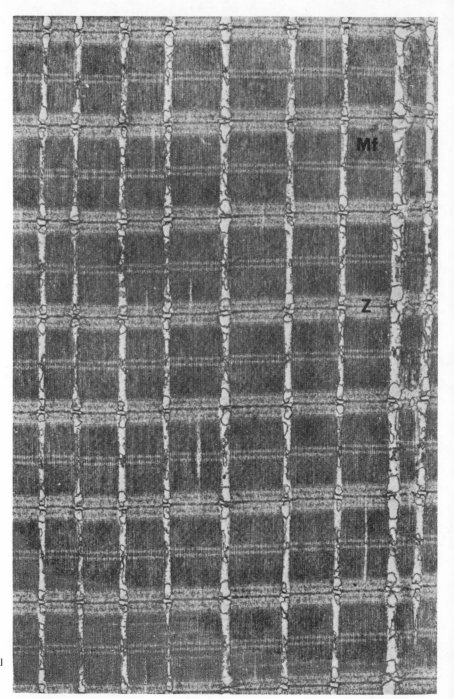

45
Structure of muscle,
revealed by the electron
microscope, from
Y. Uehara, G. R. Campbell
and G. Burnstock, *Muscle
and its Innervation*, 1976

printed on special paper of a glossy kind, and were separately bound in as copperplate engravings had had to be. Often the pictures were round or oval, and therefore have a period flavour about them. To get them into the text, it was necessary to make woodcuts from them; and this development led to the woodcut and the photograph looking more and more alike. The camera with its sensitive plate in effect had displaced the artist who had previously drawn what he saw, or perhaps drawn round the image cast on paper in a *camera lucida*. It was ironical that the artist should have been thus eliminated, while the craftsman who performed the much more mechanical task of transferring the picture to the woodblock remained in business, his ability being increasingly judged by his capacity to make the woodcut look just like the photograph. Indeed before the end of the nineteenth century the invention of the half-tone process for making metal blocks for direct printing from photographs had in turn undermined the wood engraving trade.

Half-tone blocks with their patterns of dots, and line blocks prepared mechanically from photographs, put illustrations and type again into the same press and onto the same page. But just as photography had thus led to a substitute for the woodcut, so the photograph was adapted also to the lithographic process, in photolithography. In this process a specially prepared plate — no longer of stone — is activated when the image falls on it, and can then be inked and used for printing like a lithographic plate. This process can be used for reproducing type, and has indeed led in recent years to the large-scale reprinting of books in facsimile; when it is well done, the results are very impressive. In the same way it can be used for new illustrated works, the text and pictures being disposed together and photographed, and then printed in the lithographic manner.

For black and white illustration, then, there are now two processes based on photography, which can put text and illustrations on the same page, and which do not call for a special coated paper. The same methods can be adapted, using screening to separate out the colours, for colour printing. For the finest works, some six or eight different colours will be required; thus the flower paintings made by Ferdinand Bauer in Australia in the early years of the nineteenth century have recently been printed lithographically, and the bird paintings of Henry Jones are being similarly done in a splendid edition to mark the hundred and fiftieth anniversary of the foundation of the Zoological Society of London. It is not easy to distinguish the printed Bauer illustrations from the original paintings; mechanical methods of reproduction have therefore come exceedingly close to the ideal of multiplying exact copies of what the artist drew — though one should note that our ancestors have sometimes made similar remarks about methods we would now regard as pretty unsatisfactory. We should also note that these very high quality printings do require the exercise of considerable judgement on the part of the printer, and cannot be done completely automatically.

A different method of photographic printing was developed in the 1880s known as collotype; this has been used ever since for some of the most delicate of natural history illustrations. A plate, originally of glass but now of metal, is coated uniformly with gelatine impregnated with potassium dichromate, which is light-sensitive. Full-size negatives are made from the original drawing, and then in colour printing the colours are separated, with perhaps as many as thirteen colours being used. When light shines through the negative, it hardens the dichromate; and the harder the dichromate has become, the more ink it will accept on printing. Instead of patterns of dots more or less close together giving different densities of colour, in collotype there is a continuous process giving an infinite variety of tones. The negatives can be retouched, and the final prints touched in with varnish, as required; and when well done this process can produce astonishingly fine results. It has been used for two magnificent recent publications by the British Museum (Natural History): an edition of fishes drawn on Captain Cook's voyages, and a collection of some of the pictures of plants and animals drawn in China in the early years of the nineteenth century for John Reeves, an Inspector of Teas at Canton for the East India Company. Collotype can also be used for black and white illustrations, where its continuous variety of tones is again very valuable for reproducing delicate drawings; but it is a process confined to the more expensive kind of illustrated works.

Because this is a book about illustrated zoological books, we need not concern ourselves much about the media used in the original drawings or paintings from which the published illustrations were prepared. We need only note that certain techniques and media will lend themselves better to printing by certain methods; and that no doubt it is wise for the artist to bear in mind the medium in which his illustrations are going to be printed. Having now thus run briefly through the purposes and techniques of zoological illustration from the Renaissance to the present day, we shall turn to a more strictly chronological approach, placing illustrated works in their context, and beginning with the period up to the triumph of the Linnean system in the mid-eighteenth century.

Bibliography

Where the catalogues of great libraries are published, as for example are those of the British Museum Library (now the British Library), the Library of Congress, and the Bibliotheque Nationale, these are very helpful for bibliographic information. The enormous *National Union Catalog* covering the leading libraries in the United States is similarly useful. Also very convenient are the catalogues put out by antiquarian booksellers; some issue catalogues of natural history items from time to time, while others – notably Wheldon & Wesley and the Bow Windows Bookshop, Lewes – specialise in this field and produce quarterly catalogues; good booksellers give detailed descriptions of the books they have for sale in their lists.

Bradbury, S., and Turner, G. L'E. (eds.), *Historical Aspects of Microscopy*, 1967

Bland, D., *The Illustration of Books*, 1951;
  A History of Book Illustration, 2nd edn, 1969

Bloy, C. H., *History of Printing Ink*, 1967

Carter, H., *History of the Oxford University Press*, Oxford 1975–

Chalmers-Hunt, J. M., *Natural History Auctions, 1700–1972*, 1976

Clair, C., *A Chronology of Printing*, 1969
  A History of European Printing, 1976

Coates, A., *The Book of Flowers*, 1973
  The Treasury of Flowers, 1975

Colman, D. C., *The British Paper Industry, 1495–1860*, Oxford 1958

Daumas, A., *Scientific Instruments of the 17th and 18th centuries and their Makers*, 1972

Grose, B. D., *The Antiquarian Booktrade*, Metuchen, N. J. 1972

Guggisberg, C. A. W., *Early Wildlife Photographers*, Newton Abbot 1977

Harley, R. D., *Artists' Pigments, c. 1600–1835*, 1970

Hind, A. M., *A History of Engraving and Etching*, 1923;
  An Introduction to the History of the Woodcut, 2 vols, 1935

Hosking, E., and Gooders, J., *Wildlife Photography*, 1973

Hullmandel, C., *The Art of Drawing on Stone*, 1824

Jackson, C. E., *Bird Illustrators . . . in Lithography*, 1975

James, L., *Print and the People, 1819–1851*, 1976

Landwehr, J., *Studies in Dutch Books with Coloured Plates, 1662–1875*, The Hague 1976

Lewis, R. H., *The Book Browser's Guide*, Newton Abbot 1975

Moxon, J., *Mechanick Exercises, 1677–83*; section on printing, H. Carter and H. Davis (eds.), 2nd edn, 1962

Plant, M., *The European Book Trade*, 2nd edn, 1965
  The English Book Trade, 3rd edn, 1974

Robinson, F. G. J., and Wallis, P. J., *Book Subscription Lists — a Revised Guide*, Newcastle-upon-Tyne 1975

Shorter, A. H., *Papermaking in the British Isles*, Newton Abbot 1971

Smith, D. C., *History of Papermaking in the United States, 1691–1969*, Harrow 1970

Steinberg, S. H., *Five Hundred Years of Printing*, 2nd edn, Harmondsworth 1961

Taubert, S., *The Book Trade of the World*, Hamburg 1972–

Thomson, A. G., *The Paper Industry in Scotland 1590–1861*, Edinburgh 1974

Twyman, M., *Lithography, 1800–1850*, 1970

Vervliet, H. D. L., (ed.), *The Book, Through Five Thousand Years*, 1972

Wakeman, G., and Bridson, G. D. R., *Guide to Nineteenth Century Colour Printers*, Loughborough 1975

Weatherill, L., *One Hundred Years of Papermaking*, Edinburgh 1974

For descriptions and illustrations of technical processes, nineteenth-century encyclopedias are a very valuable source; the various methods of printing illustrations are usually described there in some detail.

3

Zoological works to
the time of Linnaeus

The modern scientific naming of animals begins with the tenth edition of the *Systema Naturae* of Linnaeus, published in 1758; and only names published since that date in binomial form (where the first word designates the genus and the second is the specific or trivial name) count as valid. Taxonomists have to refer back continually to the works of Linnaeus to check the names of animals; but they do not need to go back further, because earlier names — even if used by Linnaeus in earlier works — are designated 'pre-Linnean' and have no weight for systematic purposes. A zoologist today may consult a pre-Linnean work, but in doing so he will be looking back across a watershed. The latter years of Linnaeus' life thus form a stopping place for this chapter; we will be concerned with the revival of zoology, as seen through illustrated works published from the invention of printing down to the second half of the eighteenth century.

Although we shall not find modern names in pre-Linnean works — or not often, although Linnaeus took binomial names from his predecessors when he found them — we shall discover many things of interest to the modern zoologist who is concerned, for example, with animal distribution or behaviour. He will be enquiring not simply about what name was first applied to an animal, but in a more genuinely historical manner looking at these works as documents, the reliability of which must be assessed as evidence for a past state of affairs. Often they are attractive documents, strikingly and sometimes sumptuously illustrated, and with a text that is refreshingly far from the dry and concise style of the modern paper or textbook. These very differences cannot but remind us that these writings had rather different purposes and contexts from those of modern zoological works, and that we shall miss much if we approach them simply in our own terms.

By comparison with the physical sciences, zoology and botany seem less cut off from their past; works do not so rapidly go out of date, and the great classics are still read rather than placed upon a shelf to gather dust. Old authorities must be consulted for names and for information about distribution or behaviour of animals; and so it has always been. The first zoological works that were printed in the sixteenth century indeed often seem to display more erudition than observation. This seems to have been characteristic of much Renaissance science; for there was a general belief in the *prisca sapientia*, or ancient wisdom. When Adam in the Garden of Eden named the animals, his vision was still unclouded by sin; and he, and his immediate descendants, still retained the godlike wisdom with which they had begun. To the prelapsarian Adam, therefore, the organic and inorganic world was an open book; and it was only gradually that mankind had lost the knowledge of how to read it aright. The depths of ignorance had been reached, according to this view of history, in the Dark Ages after Rome fell to the barbarians; and from these grim and Gothic times the men of the Renaissance felt themselves to be at last emerging.

Many of the great works of Antiquity seemed to have been almost miraculously preserved through these difficult times; and the invention of printing meant that accurate texts, faithfully reproducing the ancient wisdom, could be prepared and put into circulation. The older such works were — or seemed to be — the better; and the best that the Moderns could hope to do was to recover, rather than surpass, the knowledge of the Ancients. By the middle of the sixteenth century there were a few bold men, prepared to recognise that the ancient authors had not always agreed with one another, and that therefore it was better to follow their methods rather than their texts; but many of those who we think of as innovators — Vesalius, Harvey, or Ray — turn out to have been very respectful towards their ancient predecessors (just as Newton himself was in a different field). In modern times, the best analogy with the recovery of the ancient texts might be the appearance of Perry's black ships off Japan in 1853, making a whole culture seem obsolete in comparison with the knowledge and power thus disclosed.

There is no one date that can be given for the Renaissance that corresponds with the dramatic coming of black ships; but we do find a long period of assimilation and commentary before things began to fall into the modern pattern in which new writings supercede older ones. The invention of the microscope in the seventeenth century meant that the Moderns could see things that the Ancients could not, as the invention of printing text and illustrations meant that they could disseminate their discoveries in ways impossible in Antiquity. These innovations gave increasing confidence to the natural historians of the generation in which the Royal Society and the

46

The Garden of Eden, from
Parkinson's *Paradisus
Terrestris* (1656 edn) the
vegetable lamb of Tarrary is
prominent.

Académie des Sciences were founded, in the 1660s.

Thus by the end of the seventeenth century zoologists looked chiefly at modern works in their search for synonyms; references to Antiquity being more incidental or ornamental than essential. In the books of the sixteenth century it had been otherwise, but in the writings of the encyclopedic authors of this period and also in their illustrations, we find an agreeable mixture of observation with learning. The most famous of these men was Conrad Gesner (or Gessner as he apparently preferred to spell his name), whose *Historia Animalium* began to appear in 1551. It was embellished with numerous wood-cuts, including one of Dürer's rhinoceros, so that (it was hoped) the reader would be able to identify an animal from the text and illustration, and then read all that was known about it. In 1565 Gesner published a book on minerals and fossils, a term which then included anything dug out of the Earth. He recognised the similarities between some fossils and existing species, and put on the same plate illustrations of living and fossil sea-urchins for comparison; but he never discussed the origin of the fossil forms.

For pictures and text, Gesner drew upon the writings of some older

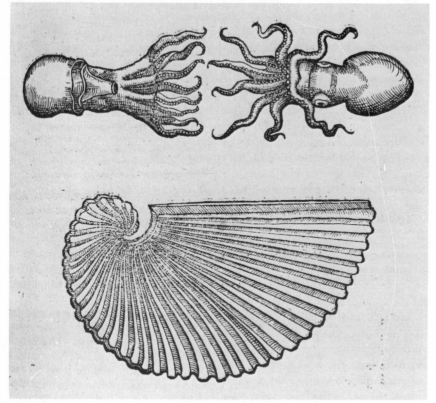

47
Squids and nautilus, from Gesner's *Historia Animalium* (1620 edn)

contemporaries; notably those of the ornithologists Pierre Belon and Rondelet, and the Scandinavian historian Olaus Magnus. Belon's *Histoire des Oiseaux* of 1555 is famous for its use of comparative anatomy in classification, and he was also a pioneer in the classification of fish. Another contemporary Ulisse Aldrovandi like Gesner was encyclopedic in his interests, and given to writing at enormous length; much of his *Historia Naturalis* was published after his death in 1605 by his disciples, but the famous three volumes on birds came out in 1599. The illustrations are very spirited, especially those of various breeds of domestic cock; Aldrovandi opened eggs at various stages of incubation, and examined skeletons as well as whole birds. Like many contemporaries, he was interested in utility, and described the practices of poultry farmers; he was also fascinated by freaks and sports of nature, such as birds with an extra foot. In these woodcut-illustrated works, the pictures are in no sense extra; they were printed with the text, and form an integral part of it.

This state of affairs was transformed in the seventeenth century when copperplate engravings began to displace woodcuts for natural history illustrations, for these are printed on a different press, often on different paper, and therefore can present difficult problems for the bibliographer. The plates could be omitted, removed, recut, and be printed or coloured at various times according to demand for the book, and therefore come in various states, the dating of which can be a problem; for publishers got more plates run off when their edition was exhausted, and sometimes had them coloured when the book was ordered, rather than before. These factors are important in determining the priority of eighteenth century publication, and are therefore not only of interest to the bibliophile; but from our point of view, we need only remark here that the value of engraved plates was that they could show greater detail. Woodcuts can be surprisingly sharp, and done by a master can very effectively catch the characteristic aspect of an animal; but they cannot display the fine structures that are used to discriminate between the various species of invertebrates or of fishes, nor those that must appear in satisfactory anatomical illustrations.

As early as 1575 Volcher Coiter had published his *Lectiones Gabrielis Fallopii* at Nuremburg, where he had returned after studying at Montpellier and Bologna, which were (with Padua) the great centres of medical education in Europe. His work contains engravings and is a pioneer study on comparative anatomy covering all vertebrate groups except fishes. Engravings were used for such standard works of the seventeenth century as John Jonston's *de Avibus* of 1650–5, and the *Ornithology* of Francis Willughby and John Ray, which appeared in English in 1678. Jonston was born in Poland, but studied at St. Andrew's and at Cambridge before settling in Leyden and ultimately returning to Silesia. His book on birds is only part of a multi-volume compilation covering all vertebrates, which was illustrated by engravings by Merian and translated into many languages; Jonston was unoriginal, but did not pretend to be otherwise for he included good references to his sources. Merian is chiefly known as the father of a very talented daughter, Maria Sybille, who in 1705 published a splendidly-illustrated volume on insects from Surinam, where she had spent two years.

John Ray on the other hand was a very original naturalist indeed, and his works were never mere compilations. William Turner, a correspondent of Gesner, had been the first English zoologist of distinction; but it was with Ray and his generation that the strong tradition of natural history in Britain really began. One step in the change from the encyclopedias of the Renaissance to the critical and empirical writings of later zoologists was the sceptical analysis of the traditions that had been inherited. The most famous such work was Sir Thomas Browne's *Pseudoxia Epidemica*, an analysis in English of the 'vulgar errors' of his contemporaries. Browne, sometimes by observation at first or second hand but often by argument alone, exploded a whole range of zoological beliefs, for example that the beaver bit off his testicles to escape the hunter, that the deer lived for over a century, that the toad had a jewel in its head, and that griffins and the phoenix really existed. Browne could hardly illustrate his book (which came out in 1646) with pictures of animals or zoological anecdotes in which he could not believe; and although Edward Topsell's *Four-footed Beasts*, a compilation based chiefly upon Gesner, was published in a new edition in 1658, one can say that Browne's exposition of 'vulgar errors' banished mythical beasts from works of science.

John Ray is perhaps chiefly remembered as a botanist and his zoological work was done in association with his patron and friend Willughby. They produced two very important illustrated works, one on fish and the other on birds; the latter volume, which Ray translated into English, remained a standard work for over a century. The illustrations are less lively than the best of Aldrovandi's, and sometimes the bird is shown as a manifest corpse; while Ray used the internal parts of birds in his classification, he did not illustrate the anatomy of the birds described. Some of the plates show details of beaks, notably of hornbills.

Some of the plates in this *Ornithology* were taken from earlier authorities; the day was yet distant when all the plates in a book would be taken afresh from actual specimens. Some were taken from unpublished pictures, notably from those assembled by Leonhardt Baldner in what he called his *Vogel Fisch und Thierbuch*. Baldner was a forester of Strasburg, and his manuscript work represents the first description of a regional fauna in Europe; Willughby and Ray bought a set from him on their continental tour of 1663–6; another set has recently been published in superb facsimile. Numerous institutions and libraries have such manuscript illustrations, which may or may not be of significance in the history of zoology, depending on whether or not they have been used in the published description or depiction of an animal. Another example of a fine set from which some pictures have recently been published is Olof

The Roller.

Garrulus Argentoratensis.
The Roller.

Garrulus Bohemicus.

Pica Brasiliensis Touam.

Caryocatactes.

TAB. XX.

48
Miscellaneous birds from
Willughby's *Ornithology*
(1678)

Rudbeck's *Fågelbok*, which consists of drawings of Scandinavian birds made between 1693 and 1710; these were used by Linnaeus.

The idea that a book or a picture was in some sense the intellectual property of its author, and that he should retain some rights over it, was slow in coming. Gesner, who had admirers at court, was indeed granted a monopoly for his writings within the Holy Roman Empire for a period of ten years; this was equivalent to a kind of copyright. There were no international agreements covering copyright, and editions of books were frequently brought out, actually or supposedly abroad, without the author's knowledge or consent. By the nineteenth century this abuse had begun to seem like piracy, but 'pirated' Dublin editions throughout the eighteenth century, and American ones in the nineteenth, were a feature of scientific as well as general publishing. In Britain, copyright for plates was introduced from 1735 (8 George II, Cap.XIII), under

49
A stilt, from White's *Selborne* (1789); this, the only zoological plate in the first edition, is dated Novr.1.1788 'as the Act directs'

an Act of Parliament which gave fourteen years protection, and was later supplemented in various ways. This statute no doubt cut down the practice of borrowing somebody else's illustrations; for the bibliographer or systematist, it was important because on an engraving so copyrighted there are words to the effect 'published as the Act directs', with the name of the publisher and the date. The date is not always to be completely trusted, but is as a rule valuable evidence especially when a work has appeared gradually and the date on the title page represents merely the first or last part. Another form of piracy was to publish a man's lectures from notes without his consent, something which happened to Boerhaave, the eminent Dutch botanist and chemist; but as a rule the threat of such action was enough to drive an eminent lecturer into publishing his own version.

By the 1660s, then, the fabulous monsters had disappeared from science, and men like Ray had begun to go beyond the achievements of their predecessors in Antiquity. Topsell's *Four-footed Beasts* studied animals in alphabetical order, like an encyclopedia, while Willughby and Ray dealt with birds in their natural groups so that the crow, the jackdaw, the raven and the rook are all described in the same chapter. The encyclopedic approach in science had become obsolete, as scientific knowledge was seen to be progressive and cumulative. Naturalists were also armed with a new instrument, the microscope, which soon proved that it could lead to discoveries as dramatic as those made with the telescope. Robert Hooke's *Micrographia* of 1665 is justly famous for its magnificent plates of the flea and the louse; nearly forty years later Leeuwenhoek, with higher magnifications, observed bacteria and protozoa and illustrated his papers with less striking, but equally interesting, engravings.

Leeuwenhoek's discoveries were published in the *Philosophical Transactions* of the Royal Society, a body in which Hooke played a prominent part. The Society had begun to meet in 1660 and had received Royal Charters in 1662 and 1663, though the patronage of King Charles II did not extend to financial assistance. It therefore became a large group all of whom were no doubt interested in science to some degree, but only a few of whom devoted time and energy to research. Partly in imitation of the Royal Society, the Académie des Sciences was founded in Paris; here a few experts were selected and salaried by the State, and were expected to turn their attention to matters of public utility when asked to do so. Both bodies began to publish semi-official journals in the 1660s, the *Philosophical Transactions* and the *Journal des Scavans*; journals which form a landmark because they transformed scientific publication.

The coming of the journals meant that anybody who had made a discovery could get it rapidly published, without waiting until he had enough material to fill a treatise; this was a further disincentive to mere compilation, for one could now publish without it. The papers moreover were refereed, so that what was published in the journals should have been authoritative; it was unfortunate

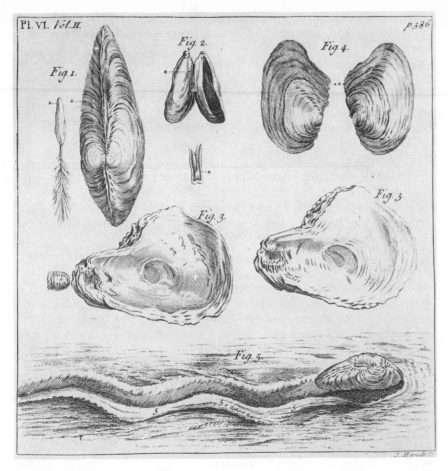

Pl. VI. *Vol. II.* p.386

Fig. 1.

Fig. 2.

Fig. 4.

Fig. 3.

Fig. 3.

Fig. 5.

50
How an oyster moves; from
*History & Memoirs of the Royal
Academy of Sciences at Paris,*
vol. 2, 1742.

perhaps that Sir Robert Moray, an early President of the Royal Society, should have published in its journal an account of the emergence of geese from barnacles.

Rather than a mass of knowledge to be ordered into an encyclopedia, the sciences were now seen as cumulative enterprises in which each scholar could add his new observations, duly confirmed by a referee, to those facts already established. It thus began to matter who first made the observation in question; disputes over priority have been a feature of the sciences since the seventeenth century. Journals, with their relatively rapid publication, should have made claims of priority easy to settle; but they were sometimes slow in publishing a particular paper, and occasionally got very much behind schedule so that sometimes a volume dated, say, 1750 might not have appeared until 1754 and might contain material added between these two dates. Priority disputes are not as a rule especially edifying to follow, except perhaps to the social historian of science; though they do reveal the competitiveness of the enterprise, and often have international implications. There was thus some Anglo-French argument in the 1820s over the discovery and description of the Malay tapir, a creature described in Chinese literature several centuries earlier. Where the priority question can be more interesting is when theoretical points are involved; for then the two claimants will almost certainly have had different interests and objectives. But usually here, as for example with the theory of evolution, the important point lies less in the first thinking of something, and more in the persuading of one's contemporaries to take it seriously.

The first journals were general, and it was not until the latter part of the eighteenth century that specialised journals, devoted to one science only, or specialised societies for that matter, appeared upon the scene. The *Philosophical Transactions* was illustrated with copperplates and although for its first century its format was only small quarto, it did sometimes contain fold-out plates so that larger drawings could be reproduced. The value of journals, whether published privately or by societies, was that a captive audience of subscribers underwrote the costs of printing and distribution, so that there was no risk of the publisher being left with expensive and unsaleable material on his hands. A similar end was achieved when books were published by subscription. There are some societies today which publish books rather than journals for their members; the prime example of this in the field of natural history is the Ray Society, but that process did not begin until the nineteenth century.

Long before that, in fact from the early seventeenth century in England, books of all kinds had been published by subscription. Somebody, usually the author, would induce a sufficiently large number of people to put their names down for the book to make it reasonably certain that publication would pay. Nehemiah Grew, the eminent contemporary of Ray, published his account of the Royal Society's museum — handsomely illustrated — in this way. Robinson and Wallis have published a guide to book subscription lists and the historian can learn much from the list of subscribers, which was as a rule printed at the front of the volume. From such a list in a work of natural history we can, for example, tell whether it was chiefly purchased by men doing zoology, or by country gentlemen and clergymen, or by doctors, or by noblemen and nabobs; and this will help us to evaluate the text and the illustrations by illuminating the author's intentions. Often an author seems to have succeeded in appealing to a wide range of interest groups, as for example did many of the authors of natural histories of English counties who followed the example of Robert Plot's publication of *Oxfordshire* in 1677.

Many works of zoology were published by subscription, and indeed still are; the handsome edition of the *Bird Paintings of Henry Jones*, for example, was announced and subscriptions invited in 1976; any copies unsubscribed were to be sold after publication at a higher price than that paid in advance by the

84

subscribers. Eighteenth-century publishers did not usually get the money, or all of it, in advance, and tales of the pursuit of defaulting subscribers are common especially where the book appeared some years after it had been announced. A particular problem with large and handsome works, probably illustrated in colour, was that the cost could daunt the subscriber, while the amount of capital required could be too much for the publisher. The solution was to publish the work in parts; and that was how many of the great illustrated works in zoology of the eighteenth and nineteenth centuries did appear, one of the early and very famous ones being Mark Catesby's *Natural History of Carolina*, of 1731–43.

A book published in parts occupies a half-way position between an ordinary book and a journal; and indeed libraries nowadays sometimes have problems with apparently endless 'continuations' when the fauna or flora of some region is being gradually described. The author might like Catesby (and Gould a century after him) be his own publisher, undertaking to produce at regular intervals, parts containing so much text and so many illustrations, and also to forecast how many parts there would be altogether. In pre-inflationary times, he also undertook to provide the parts at a certain price. Catesby moreover was his own etcher, and closely supervised the colouring of the plates; but the timetable of publication could easily get disturbed, especially where engravers and colourists not under the author's control were involved. There is an amusing account by an anonymous inveterate subscriber, of the problems and annoyances involved from his point of view, in the *Magazine of Natural History, 3* (1830) 297–308; while we find the authors' problems in their biographies — what comes over clearly is that though some natural historians, like Gould, have been excellent businessmen, many have not.

One could hardly imagine subscribers to Euclid buying from him theorems in random order, one at a time, and afterwards having them bound up into a set of the *Elements of Geometry*; but the logic of natural history is less rigorous than that of geometry, and also the exigencies of the subject forced this method of publication on authors. The major illustrated works in zoology of the eighteenth century were regional studies or accounts of vast families of creatures, rather than monographs on some circumscribed natural group; and as the work proceeded the author would usually come across species that he had not known about when he began to write. It was indeed an advantage of part publication that after some parts had come out anybody interested would know to whom to send the skin of a curious bird. When the work was completed, or just stopped as these things sometimes did (Lear's great work on parrots is a magnificent example of a work that was unfinished), the author would issue a title page and index, perhaps at no extra charge, and the purchaser would then have the book suitably bound.

The binder would then take to bits the various parts or fascicles, which would have been stitched with stab holes, and bind them up in accordance with the 'directions for the binder' that accompanied the index. This was a tricky business for many binders even when all that was required was to place the plates correctly within a single volume, as anyone familiar with eighteenth-century books will know — often one plate at least is out of place, by accident or perhaps because the owner decided to put in a frontispiece. In multi-volume sets that appeared in parts the plates tend to be disordered and are mere approximations of the intentions of the original compiler; there may even be no ideal set in existence. Some owners, at the time or later, may not have shared the author's views on classification, and therefore deliberately arranged the plates and descriptions in a different order from that recommended. All this makes it difficult and fascinating to determine in what order the parts were published, because two successive plates may have originally appeared in the first and last parts, perhaps ten years apart. If a plate was

51
List of plates, from Cook's *Voyage towards the South Pole* (1778); the numbering here is unusually confusing, for a book not published in parts

LIST of the PLATES,

With DIRECTIONS for placing them.

[As the Plates, for the fake of expedition, were printed off as faft as they were finifhed, it was neceffary to number them, before any confideration could be had of the proper arrangement. They are to be placed in the following order.]

VOL. I.

Page.		Plate.
	Print of Captain Cook fronts the Title-page.	
1	Chart of the Southern Hemifphere, fhewirg Captain Cook's tracks, and thofe of fome of the moft diftinguifhed navigators	I.
8	Port Praya, in the Ifland of St. Jago, one of the Cape de Verds	X.
37	View of the Ice-Iflands	XXX.
70	NewZealand fpruce	LI.
75	Family in Dufky-Bay, New Zealand	LXIII.
92	Sketch of Dufky Bay, New Zealand	XIII.
96	Flax plant of New Zealand	XXIII.
97	Poi Bird of New Zealand	LII.
100	Tea Plant of New Zealand	XXII.
115	Van Diemen's Land	VIII.
154	Otoo King of Otaheite	XXXVIII.
157	Plant ufed at Otaheite to catch fifh by intoxicating them	XXIV.
159	Potatow, Chief of Attahourou, in Otaheite	LVI.
169	Omai, who was brought to England by Captain Furneaux	LVII.
181	View of Otaheite Ifland	LIII.
185	A Tupapow with a corpfe	XLIV.

9

Page

early, it might have priority for purposes of naming; while if it were late, it would be a mere synonym.

While zoology did not, then, have such magnificently produced journals as botany did from the late eighteenth century — except perhaps for some periodicals of the nineteenth century devoted to field sports, which have always had a close but uneasy realtionship to the science — its great works produced in parts had something of the same character. They came out more or less regularly, and were self-financing in that receipts from part 1 paid for the production of part 2 and so on, and they were regularly sold to a list of subscribers that changed little. For more systematic works, which more resembled Euclid in being one long argument which must all hang together, this method of publication was unsuitable; so that while monographs for example might come out by subscription, they did not as a rule come out in parts.

A monograph by a contemporary of Ray and Grew was Edward Tyson's *Orang-Outang* of 1699. This book, with its famous plates illustrating the dissection of what was in fact a chimpanzee, remained for over a century a model study; for its was only in the middle of the nineteenth century that the anthropoid apes came to be really seriously studied, in researches that received a further impetus from the Darwinian controversy after 1859. The term 'orang-outang' is from the Malay and means 'man of the woods', and was used loosely as a generic term; Tyson recognised that his creature was not a man, and believed that old stories about pygmies, satyrs, and cynocephali (men with dog's heads) were really jumbled accounts of apes and monkeys. Some of his followers were less certain; thus Lord Monboddo in his *Ancient Metaphysics* (6 vols, 1779–99) suggested that these great apes were genuine wild men, having perhaps superior moral qualities to those of civilised Europeans. This view was satirised in Peacock's novel *Melincourt*, published in 1817, where the amiable Sir Oran Haut-ton plays a notable role; he is superior to the human characters except that he lacks the gift of language.

The drawings in Tyson's book, and also the account of the muscles, were by William Cowper, an anatomist who also worked with Tyson on other anatomical studies. Tyson himself was physician to the famous Bethlehem Hospital, or Bedlam, for lunatics, where he apparently introduced a regime that was humane and unrepressive for its day. This reminds us again that even the most eminent of anatomists could not live by his scientific work alone in this period; the sciences in 1700 were still something to be pursued in one's spare time, and while Tyson's work was not amateurish he was certainly not a professional scientist.

From the sixteenth century onwards, the exploration of distant parts of the world became an increasingly important part of natural history. While some eminent naturalists, such as Linnaeus, did not travel into different zoological provinces, many others did; and right down to the time of Darwin, Wallace,

52
Chimpanzee, from Tyson's
Orang-outang (1699)

88

and Huxley a visit to a remote region was a prudent step on the way to zoological fame and fortune. The first such scientific traveller in Britain might be the polymath Thomas Hariot, whose *Briefe and True Report of the New Found Land of Virginia* (1588) — essentially propaganda for the colony set up by his patron Raleigh — includes descriptions of the animals, birds and fish to be found there. Hariot emphasises those creatures that are good to eat; the turkey is among those mentioned, and it is one of the curiosities of the history of zoology that this bird was so long supposed to be from the east — hence its name. The pictures of Indians done by John White were engraved and published at the same time by Theodore de Bry; but the zoological illustrations he made were used by other authors such as Topsell and later Catesby, but not published until 1964.

Hariot's most important work was in mathematics, physics, and astronomy. He was interested in the atomic theory long before it was 'revived' by Gassendi and Boyle in the middle of the seventeenth century, and he looked at the moon with a telescope before Galileo. Much the same could be said of some eminent successors of Hariot in zoological work, such as Maupertuis and Réaumur in eighteenth-century France; but in general specialisation came in with the rise of scientific societies and academies, so that later zoologists often worked also in botany and geology, but rarely in astronomy and physics, beyond perhaps observing for latitude and longitude on their travels.

Newton's Presidency of the Royal Society from 1703 to 1727 had set the fashion both for choosing as president a man of science who had published important work, rather than someone highly-placed and well-connected; and also for presidents to serve for a long time. His successor was a natural historian, which was not surprising because astronomy and mathematical physics were carried on too much in Newton's shadow and declined in the years following his death, whereas the descriptive and experimental sciences flourished in Britain. Sir Hans Sloane, who was president from 1727 to 1741, was a physician who had made his scientific reputation with a voyage to the West Indies from 1687 to 1689, which he wrote up in two sumptuous volumes, *A Voyage to the Islands Madera, Barbados, Nieves, St Christopher's and Jamaica*, published in 1707–25.

Sloane was one of the patrons of Mark Catesby who went from England to describe the natural history of Carolina; Catesby, like Lewin and J. V. Thompson after him, cut out the engraver and prepared his own plates. This step saved money, but perhaps such author-engravers would have agreed with the eighteenth century French engraver, Charles-Nicholas Cochin Jr., who said: 'On ne doit pas regarder les excellents graveurs comme des simples copistes, ce sont plutôt les traducteurs qui font passer les beautés d'une langue très riche dans une autre qui l'est moins', and preferred to be their own translators.

The works of Sloane and of Catesby were the first regional studies of their

53   Cabbage white butterflies, from Lewin's *Papilios* (1795), drawn and engraved by the author

areas, and hence formed the basis for all later work. They were applying to a foreign country the approach which Robert Plot had followed in his studies of English counties. Scientific travel was not a monopoly of any one country; as one would expect, Britain's naval rivals, Holland and France, also produced natural historians who wrote illustrated works on distant countries. Thus W. Piso and G. Marcgrave accompanied Prince Maurice of Nassau when he was governor of the Dutch colony in north-eastern Brazil from 1637 to 1644; the colony, run by the West India Company, was a short-lived affair, lasting only from 1624 to 1654. Piso went as a physician and described the diseases and remedies of the country; while Marcgrave, who had been appointed as an astronomer, wrote up the botany and zoology. Their composite work, *Historia Naturalis Brasiliae*, was published at the expense of Prince Maurice in folio in 1648, Marcgrave having died in Africa where he had gone soon after getting back to Holland in 1644. The book was illustrated with woodcuts; of these Albert Günther, who was not easy to please, remarked that they 'are not good, but nearly always recognisable, giving a fair idea of the form of the fish' — for the descriptions of fishes are particularly important. The original paintings, which give a much better idea of the species, were used for example by Mark Bloch in his account of foreign fish of 1785–95, and later; they have been missing since the Second World War, but there is still hope that they are in existence.

Later writers in the Dutch service who wrote on the natural history of Surinam, or Dutch Guiana, included Maria Merian, whose splendid plates of insects and other creatures are famous; and Edward Bancroft a surgeon from Massachusetts, whose *Natural History* of 1769 has a frontispiece of a two-headed snake allegedly seen in North America; and John Gabriel Stedman from the Scots Brigade of mercenaries sent to put down a slave revolt between 1772 and 1777. Ironically Stedman's sympathies were with the rebels, and in Surinam he lived with a beautiful mulatto, Joanna, who bore him a son but whom he could not afford to redeem and emancipate on his departure. Stedman's book, which finally appeared in 1796, described the natural history of the region, and was illustrated with eighty plates, some of which were engraved by William Blake. Meanwhile in the Dutch East Indies natural history was not neglected; Kaempfer visited Japan, and wrote what became the standard work on its natural history in the West until the mid nineteenth century, and Rumpf produced in 1705 his work on the natural history of Amboina, handsomely illustrated especially with plates of shells. A little later in 1724–6 Francois Valentijn, who had had his enthusiasm for natural history kindled by Rumpf, published his account of the natural history of Amboina, describing among other things the King Bird of Paradise.

Right through the eighteenth century, France remained the greatest centre for science in Europe; and French travellers and explorers played an important part in adding to zoological knowledge. Leguat was a Huguenot who had

54 Butterfly and bananas, from Merian's *Metamorphosis Insectorum Surinamensium* (1719 edn)

to leave France on the revocation of the Edict of Nantes and he went with other refugees to Rodriguez, a remote island in the Indian Ocean east of Mauritius. In 1708 his illustrated *Voyages et Aventures*, was published, containing plates of the species of Dodo found on Rodriguez and the neighbouring islands of Mauritius and Réunion. The great botanist and friend of Sloane, Tournefort, had travelled in the Middle East; and his admirer Michel Adanson also went abroad at a crucial stage in his career. Adanson is best known as a botanist, but when in Senegal — where he went as a clerk in the service of the Compagnie des Indes — he made zoological collections too, especially of shellfish, which he described in his volume on *Coquillages*, published in 1757.

Adanson was one of the first to pay as much attention to the creature within the shell as to the shell itself; though in this he had some precursors, such as Martin Lister, to whom he gave little acknowledgement. This was one aspect

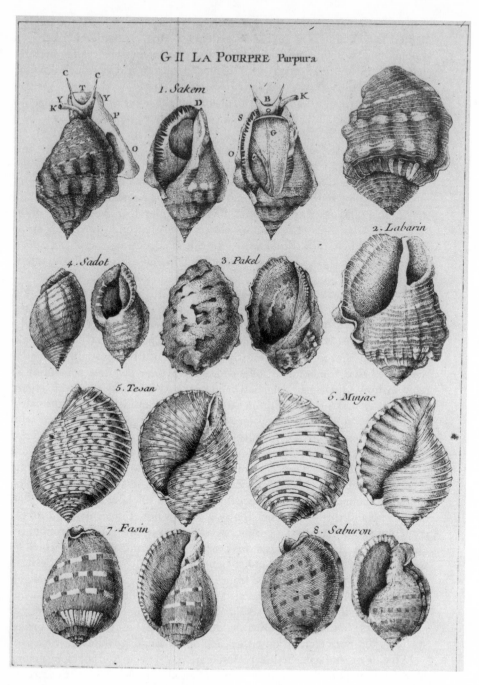

G II LA POURPRE *Purpura*

1. Sakem

2. Labarin

4. Sadot

3. Pakel

5. Tesan

6. Minjac

7. Fasin

8. Saburon

55   Shells, from Adanson's *Coquillages* (1757)

of his determination to make classification a matter of finding the natural method rather than of applying an artificial system. A distinction between systems and method was one not confined to the life sciences in the later eighteenth century; indeed critics of the mechanical world view including the chemist Humphry Davy, and the philosopher-poet S. T. Coleridge divided chemical theories into good and bad ones in the same way. In zoology, a system was a pragmatically justified way of classifying animals, based upon a single character or a small group of characters. The natural method, by contrast, meant the assessment of all characters in order to determine how nature — that potent demiurge for the eighteenth century — had really grouped animals into families. It was therefore legitimate to classify molluscs simply according to their shells if one were pursuing a system; but if one's aim were higher, and one was looking for the real families, then the anatomy of the shell's inhabitant was of equal importance. For Adanson, it was not possible even to weight characters differently, for this in effect was to apply an *a priori* system; after the classes had been determined upon the basis of all characters, then some could be more heavily weighted for diagnostic purposes.

The problem with the natural system was that it was provisional, in that characters nobody had thought of bothering about or had been able to see before might, when duly considered, upset the existing arrangement. On the whole, most of Adanson's contemporaries in the English and German speaking worlds preferred to use the artificial system of Linnaeus, although they recognised that sometimes it offended against their intuitive perception of relationships. Older men, who had been brought up on Ray's natural system, preferred stick to that, with its rather different families; and Adanson did not make acceptance of his system easier by his tendency to quarrel with eminent contemporaries, especially later in his life when suitable posts seemed to have been blocked for him. A further difficulty in the reception of his work was that he preferred to use local names for animals and plants; for example he used Wolof names for his discoveries in Senegal, and was even unhappy when Linnaeus named the baobab tree 'Adansonia' in his honour. We would no doubt applaud this as evidence that a man was not ethnocentric; but to his contemporaries it seemed a curious devotion to barbaric and unpronounceable usages, and Adanson has to his credit a large number of names which he was in fact the first to assign but which never came into use and have been set aside. Even with names derived from Latin, Greek, or European languages, Adanson preferred his own reformed spelling, 'Kokillajes' for 'Coquillages' being an example; in this he resembled his younger contemporary, the physicist Thomas Young, who spelled the mineral 'Yttria' as 'itria', but reformed spellings did not catch on on either side of the English Channel.

In trying to establish a natural classification, Adanson was not alone among his countrymen; Buffon was an example of another zoologist who tried to base his families upon a wide ranger of characters, despite the provisional nature of

56   Bats, from Buffon's
Histoire Naturelle
(Supplément, 1774–79)

such a method and the fears expressed in Britain that such an arrangement must sink beneath its own weight. As Keeper of the Jardin du Roi and of the Royal Cabinet, Buffon had splendid opportunities to produce his great work describing the complete animal kingdom, as he did in his *Histoire Naturelle, Générale et Particulière* which began to appear in 1749 and continued after Buffon's death in 1788, the last eight volumes of the forty-four being completed by Lacépède. This great compilation — for, unlike Adanson, Buffon did not visit an exotic region or perform profound researches into any one family of creatures — summed up the work of pre-Linnean natural historians (and some post-Linnean ones in the later volumes), and was illustrated with engravings. There were various translations of it, and the work became very widely known, spreading the taste for natural history very widely throughout Europe and North America. Buffon, like Adanson, was not convinced that species were unchanging; he believed that 'degeneration' had taken place, and in a celebrated war of words with Jefferson he urged that this process had gone on more rapidly in America than in Europe. The point was that there seemed to be fossils there of much larger creatures, such as Jefferson's *megalonyx*, than now existed; which might imply (except to a resolute patriot like Jefferson) that America was an enervating environment.

The writings of travellers, and Buffon's compilation (and popularisations such as Goldsmith's *Animated Nature* of 1774), made it evident how different were the fauna of different parts of the world. Similar climates often supported a quite different set of animals and plants, indicating that the globe was a more diverse place than might have been expected. This fact was seized upon by some natural theologians, such as William Derham, author of the famous work *Physico-Theology*; the book was based upon a course of sermon-lectures endowed under the will of Robert Boyle, the great chemist who believed that the existence and benevolence of God could be demonstrated from the study of nature. Ray had also written in this genre, but his book and Derham's were unillustrated; at a later date we shall come across natural theologies with plates, for these works remained popular, especially in Britain, down to the middle of the nineteenth century. The geographical distribution of animals was thus seen in the first half of the eighteenth century in terms of God's delight in variety; the contrast was made with mechanical processes turning out lots of things which were all the same.

This divine delight in variety was closely related to the idea of God's creation of a Great Chain of Being, stretching from crystals up to men and on through the orders of angels. One of the difficulties about this view was its timelessness. God, in creating as wide a range of things as possible in order to make the best of all possible worlds, would have been expected to have all the different types of creature in it at the same time; if something were to die out, then the world would become less than the best possible, and if something new were to come into being then this would mean that the world had been less

96

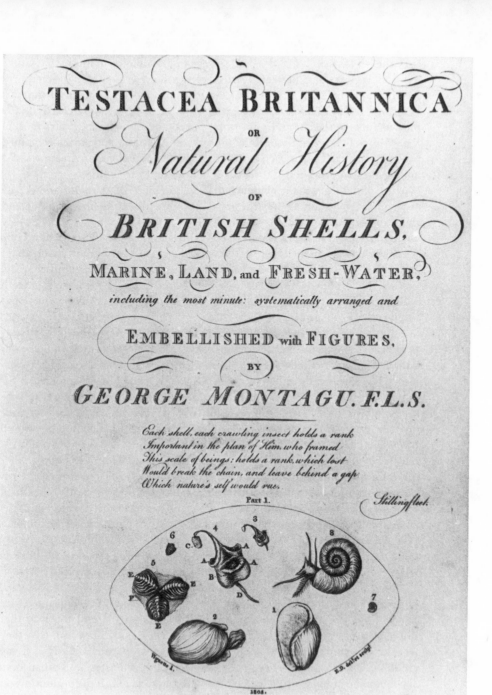

TESTACEA BRITANNICA

OR

Natural History

OF

BRITISH SHELLS,

MARINE, LAND, and FRESH-WATER,

including the most minute: systematically arranged and

EMBELLISHED with FIGURES,

BY

GEORGE MONTAGU. F.L.S.

Each shell, each crawling insect holds a rank
Important in the plan of Him, who framed
This scale of beings: holds a rank, which lost
Would break the chain, and leave behind a gap
Which nature's self would rue.

Stillingfleet.

Part 1.

1803.

57   Engraved title page for part 1 of Montagu's *Testacea Britannica* (1803); note the verse about the
Great Chain of Being.

97

than the best possible so far — and to urge that, would be to imply that God's foresight was less than perfect. The idea of an infinite variety of living creatures forming a Great Chain was difficult to apply to the families of animals described by travellers and zoologists at home; for there were clearly many missing links in the chain. By the latter part of the eighteenth century most of the world was known, though the interiors of Australia and Africa remained mysterious; and it became clear that there were not many more missing links, among the larger animals at least, to be found.

More daunting was the evidence that certain kinds of animals had become extinct. Marine animals are the most likely creatures to be fossilised, and shellfish form the most abundant fossils. It was an advantage, curiously enough, of the systems of classification which Adanson criticised, that if one were working from shells alone then there were no very great problems in classifying modern and fossil species together. In the seventeenth century, despite the famous work of Steno (1669) who compared fossil shark's teeth with those from a recently-caught specimen, it was not generally accepted that similarity of form implied similarity of origin. This was especially so in Britain; in Italy there was abundance of Tertiary fossils, which were extremely similar to existing shells, while in Britain the rocks examined were usually much older and the fossils therefore bore much less resemblance to living forms. They were also often chemically different, being siliceous rather than calcareous for example; and since the term 'fossil' meant anything dug up, it might well be that many fossils in a collection were flints or other stones having an adventitious resemblance to animal remains — indeed modern palaeontologists still have their category of objects of uncertain origins, as Rudwick points out in his masterly essay on the history of palaeontology, *The Meaning of Fossils*.

Athanasius Kircher in his *Mundus Subterraneus* of 1664–5 had argued against the organic origin of fossils; against him a Sicilian naturalist, Scilla, published an illustrated essay on 'vain speculation undeceived by sense' in which he compared living and fossil shells and corals. But in Britain despite the publication of a translation of Steno's *The Prodromus to a Dissertation* in 1671 by Henry Oldenburg, Secretary of the Royal Society, many of the best naturalists remained unconvinced. The eminent naturalist Martin Lister published in 1678 his *Historia Animalium Angliae*, and between 1685 and 1697 his *Synopsis*, both being very important illustrated works on shells; but the enormous size and curious chemical composition of many fossil shells, and the way that different sorts were found in different sorts of rock, convinced him that they were of inorganic origin and he described them separately. Only if living creatures of the same species as the ammonites, belemnites, and other fossil shells could be found would he have been prepared to admit the organic origin of these stones.

In his *Natural History of Oxfordshire*, 1677, Robert Plot had a chapter on 'formed stones' in which he came to much the same conclusion; he illustrated in that book some stones which we would recognise as fossils, and others that we would regard as inorganic in origin. County histories like Plot's *Oxfordshire* and *Staffordshire*, and those of larger regions like Catesby's on the Carolinas, encouraged scholars and gentlemen to form cabinets of curiosities. Some of these collections have become the nuclei of later natural history museums; the most notable of these was Sloane's, which was left to the nation and represents the origin of the British Museum. The exchange of specimens became increasingly important as new emphasis was given to taxonomy and naming, and the examination, or re-examination, of type specimens took on a new importance. Plot's most eminent successor in the eighteenth century as a county historian, William Borlase, published his work on Cornwall in 1758 and sent specimens — mostly of minerals — to Boerhaave and Linnaeus; his book includes the first description and illustration of the Leathery Turtle in Britain, and is, as one might expect, particularly strong on marine fauna.

Works of travel and local natural histories only include zoology as one part of their field; in more modern terms, their emphasis is ecological. Thus Thomas Shaw described the fossils of the Levant in an appendix to his well-known *Travels*. It would be wrong to suppose that as natural history rapidly gained in prestige and popularity in the eighteenth century, there were no works confined to one of the natural history sciences. The various branches of zoology were all enriched with illustrated works of various degrees of splendour in the first half of the eighteenth century. Some of these were no more than compilations for children; the most famous of these was probably the *Description of Three Hundred Animals*, which is thought to have been put together by its publisher, Thomas Boreman. Though on the title page it is claimed that the material has been 'extracted from the best authors', the spirited little engravings are in fact taken from Gesner and Topsell; it is curious to see, in a book which appeared in 1730 and had an edition as late as 1786, Dürer's rhinoceros, the manticora, and the lamia appearing once more. Many of the animals have curiously human faces; the bison, the lynx, the 'bear-ape' and the 'sagoin' gaze at us in sad perplexity. Whereas Topsell's book was organised in alphabetical order, it is hard to see any sense in the arrangement of quadrupeds in Boreman's; the birds are in some kind of natural groups, perhaps because he had Willughby and Ray to guide him there. The book did first arouse Robert Jameson's interest in natural history; in which he became eminent, as Professor at Edinburgh in the early nineteenth century. A contemporary work from France, Pluche's *Spectacle de la Nature*, was more up to date, but was in the form of moralising dialogues which one might expect the young reader to have found tedious.

Also contemporary, but at a very different level, was Eleazar Albin's *Natural History of Birds*, 1731–8, which is beautifully illustrated with plates drawn and engraved by Albin and his daughter. Albin had earlier written a book on English insects, and wrote another on spiders; both of these books have

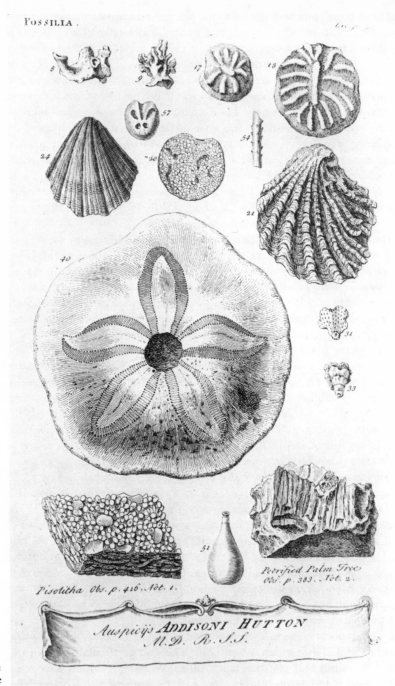

FOSSILIA.

Auspicijs *ADDISONI HUTTON*
M.D. R.S.S.

58
Fossils, from Shaw's *Travels
in the Levant* (1738); note the
dedication to a patron.

attractive and arresting illustrations and indeed though not shown against realistic backgrounds, Albin's creatures look vigorous and alive. In ornithology, his most important successor in Britain was George Edwards; who had learned from Catesby the art of engraving and etching his own plates. His *Natural History of Uncommon Birds* of 1743–51, and *Gleanings of Natural History* of 1758–64, have spirited pictures of exotic birds; they also have a bilingual text (in English and French) which was a not uncommon solution to the problem of Babel as Latin passed out of use as a common language among the learned. Even in Germany, Latin was in decline; and there J. D. Meyer published between 1748 and 1756 his book of illustrations of birds and mammals, including in the pictures the skeletons of the creatures, arranged in rather morbid and unnatural attitudes.

Albin produced, as well as his grander works, a pleasant little book on English song birds in 1737, which was so popular that it had reached a third edition by 1739. This book was written for bird fanciers, and reminds us how many wild birds our ancestors must have caught and caged. He reports that a sky lark may live for fifteen or twenty years in confinement; and he denounces the cruel custom of blinding chaffinches to make them sing more. This was therefore a book about domestic animals; and as such falls into a fairly large group covering many branches of zoology. The great French metallurgist and naturalist Réaumur wrote a work on the artificial incubation of hen's eggs; the process had been described by Thevenot, who had seen it in his travels in the Levant, but was new to Western Europe. Réaumur also wrote a book on bees, which became the standard work for most of the eighteenth century; it was extensively used by later authors, such as Thomas Wildman whose *Treatise . . . on Bees* came out in 1770.

While fish are hardly perhaps domesticated animals, they were preserved in ponds and in rivers, and works on how to rear and to catch them have a place in the literature of zoology. The literary masterpiece among them is Izaak Walton's *Compleat Angler*, which has appeared in numberless editions since it was first published in 1653, some of them very attractively illustrated. Soon after it came Robert Venables' *Experienc'd Angler*, the first edition of which was published anonymously in 1662, and was illustrated. Earlier than these two had been Gervase Markham's *Pleasure of Princes*, which appeared as part of his *English Husbandman* in 1614. Markham was an extremely prolific writer, best known for his work on horses; he was apparently the first to import an Arab horse into England to improve the breed, and in 1610 published a work of farriery, *Markham's Maister-peece*. In 1649 there appeared an anonymous illustrated work, *The English Farrier*; it was followed in 1683 by Snape's *Anatomy of an Horse*, with splendid cuts (taken from Ruini's work of 1598) of noble beasts. This work is only overshadowed by Stubbs' *Anatomy of the Horse* of 1766, with its eighteen plates showing the horse in various stages of dissection; they were drawn by Stubbs over some weeks in an isolated farmhouse in Lincolnshire,

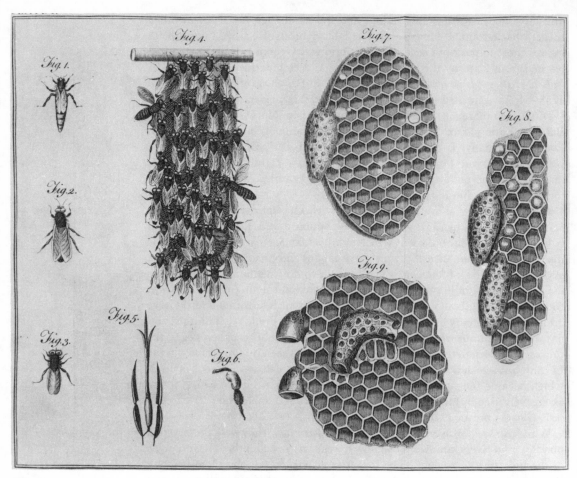

59
Bees, and their cells, from
Wildman's *Treatise on Bees*
(1778 edn)

where he worked apparently untroubled by the smell. These careful anatomical studies lay behind the superb pictures of horses and other animals that Stubbs painted.

The horses that Stubbs anatomised were dead, but vivisections had been carried out by Stephen Hales of Teddington earlier in the eighteenth century. He was a Newtonian, who sought to bring to zoology the quantitative methods of physics; and in his *Haemastaticks* of 1733 described experiments on measuring blood-pressures in horses, deer, dogs, and other animals, resulting in their deaths from loss of blood. The work, which is mercifully unillustrated, aroused the ire of Hales' friend, the poet Pope; and in the next century, it was the French — notably the 'murderous Magendie' as he was called — who were forward in practising vivisection. It may be that Hales, like other Newtonians, accepted the Cartesian doctrine that animals were mere automata,

102

and that one could not be cruel to them any more than to a clock; certainly he hoped that his work would benefit physiology and hence medicine; which is more than can be said for the illustration of how to make nightingales into a pie in Olina's ornithological book of 1622.

Markham was apparently described as the 'first English hackney writer'; among his successors was Sir John Hill in the mid eighteenth century, who was a playwright and author of works on natural history. His title has often been supposed to have been self-imposed, but it was apparently a genuine Swedish knighthood formally recognised by George II. Hill translated the *Bible of Nature* of Swammerdam, a very valuable study particularly of the life cycle of various insects; and then produced a three-volume *General Natural History*, illustrated with engravings, of his own. This became a very widely used work, particularly perhaps among those who were not themselves naturalists; it was a good compilation and popularistion rather than a work of research.

In his work on the mayfly and other creatures Swammerdam had made extensive use of the microscope. The standard work of the eighteenth century on the microscope is Baker's *Employment for the Microscope* of 1753, which illustrates various splendid but not always very practical-looking instruments. Among zoological authors who used the microscope were Bradley, whose *Philosophical Account of the Works of Nature* was published in 1821 and includes engravings of insects and animalculae, drawn in a curious *trompe d'oeil* manner to give the illusion that the various figures on the plate are drawn on separate bits of paper, pinned on to a dark ground. More important microscopic studies were those of Trembley, on polyps; he investigated the common *hydra*, showing how it propagated by budding, could be turned inside out, and so on. These researches were particularly significant because the polyps seemed to be a link between the plant and animal kingdoms, as expected by those who believed in the Great Chain of Being. Trembley's researches were described in his illustrated *Mémoires* of 1744, published in quarto in Leyden and in the same year in octavo in Paris.

Another 'missing link' of this kind was provided by the corals, of which it was hard to say whether they were animal, vegetable, or mineral. Here the classic work was done by John Ellis, in his *Essay towards an Natural History of the Corallines* of 1755. Ellis in 1754 had persuaded Ehret, the great botanical artist, to accompany him to Brighton 'there to draw from Nature, whatever the Microscope presented him of these extraordinary Beings'. The book duly contains delicate engravings from these drawings. Ellis argued for the animal nature of the corals and their allies; he relied also on some primitive chemical tests, such as that heated vegetable substance smells unpleasant, and animal substance foul. Upon the whole, these researches on polyps and corals did not close the gaps between the kingdoms of nature as some had hoped they would, for it was possible to assign them to the animal kingdom despite their appearance; this work did not therefore supply much support for the Great Chain,

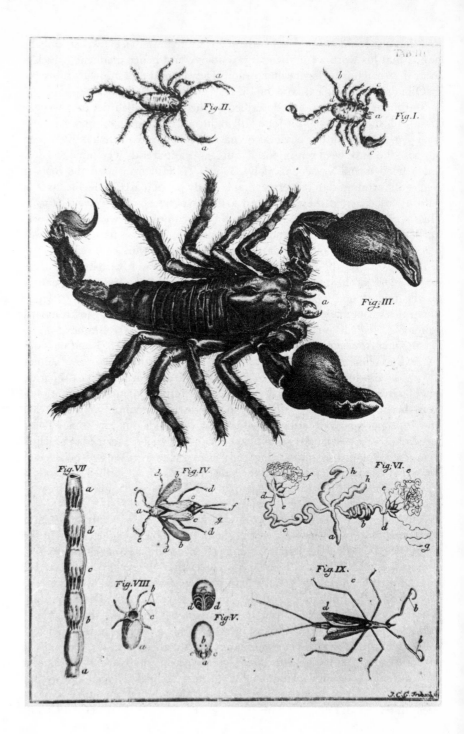

60
Scorpion, from
Swammerdam's *Book of
Nature* (1758)

Plate XVI.

61   Corallines, from Ellis' *Corallines* (1755)

though it did perhaps encourage that eighteenth-century belief in the analogy between plants and animals to which Ritterbush has recently drawn attention.

With Ellis, then, we have come to the verge of the Linnean period, in which the zoological riches of the new continent of Australasia were discovered and the interior of North and South America and of Siberia were also visited by scientific travellers. This was also a period in which wealthy patrons were prepared to support the publication of lavish works of natural history, and to subscribe to them; and in which governments were prepared to promote expeditions in which the advancement of natural history was a prominent objective. Specialised societies and proprietary journals devoted to natural history grew up; and there was a market for popular and technical works on zoology as well as for the small editions of the really magnificent works. The March of Mind, or Intellect, of the 1820s with its increase in literacy led to a demand for popular books; but the era of the textbook and the treatise had still not arrived by the 1830s where, with the death of Cuvier in 1832, we shall conclude the next chapter.

Bibliography

In the lists that follow chapters 3, 4, and 5, books by authors who flourished during the period covered by the chapters are listed, together with bibliographies of their works. Those authors whose work spans two chapters are only listed once, all their books appearing after the chapter in which their opus seems to come most appropriately. Journals are listed after the chapter covering the period in which they began publication.

Académie des Sciences, Paris, *Histoire*, 11 vols, 1666–99;
  Mémoires, 1699–1790, 93 vols, 1702–97; thereafter *Mémoires de l'Institut. Memoirs*,
  A. Pitfield (tr.), 1688; *History and Memoirs*, J. Martin (tr.), 5 vols, 1742;
  Hahn, R., *Anatomy of a Scientific Institution*, Berkeley 1971
Adams G., *Micrographia Illustrata*, 1746
Adanson, M., *Histoire Naturelle du Senégal: Coquillages*, Paris 1757
  Adanson, G. H. M. Lawrence (ed.), 2 vols, Pittsburgh 1963
Aesop, *The Fables*, W. Caxton (tr.), 1484
Albin, E., *A Natural History of English Insects*, 1720;
  A Natural History of Birds, 3 vols, 1731–8;
  A Natural History of Spiders, 1736;
  A Natural History of English Song Birds, 1737
Aldrovandi, U., *Ornithologiae*, 3 vols, Bologna 1599–1637;
  De animalium Insectis, Bologna 1602;
  De Piscibus, Bologna 1613;
  De Quadrupedibus, Bologna 1616;
  Serpentum et Draconū Historiae, Bologna 1640;
  Monstrorum Historia, Bologna 1642
Anon, *The English Farrier*, 1649
Artedi, P., *Ichthyologia*, C. Linnaeus (ed.), Leyden 1738; J. Walbaum (ed.), Grypswaldiae 1788–93

Baker, H., *An Attempt Towards a Natural History of the Polype*, 1743;
  Employment for the Microscope, 1753
Baldner, L., *Vogel- Fisch- und Thierbuch, 1666*, 2 vols, Stuttgart 1973–74
Barlaeus (K. van Baerle), C., *Rerum per Octennium in Brasilia*, Amsterdam 1647
Barlow, F., *Several Ways of Hunting, Hawking, and Fishing*, 1671;
  Various Birds and Beasts Drawn from the Life, 1690
Bartram, J., *Observations . . . in His Travels from Pensilvania*, 1751
Belon, P., *De Aquatilibus*, Paris 1553;
  L'Histoire de la Nature des Oyseaux, Paris 1555
Blackwell, E., *A Curious Herbal*, 2 vols, 1737
Bonnet, C., *Considérations sur les Corps Organisés*, 2 vols, Amsterdam 1762;
  Oeuvres, 9 vols, Neuchâtel 1779–81
Borelli, G. A., *De Motu Animalium*, 2 vols, Rome 1680–81
Boreman, T., *A Description of Three Hundred Animals*, 1730;
  A great variety of Animals and Vegetables, 1736;
  Curious and Uncommon Creatures, 1739
Borlase, W., *The Natural History of Cornwall*, Oxford 1758
Bradley, R., *A Philosophical Account of the Works of Nature*, 1721
Brisson, M. J., *Ornithologie*, 6 vols, Paris 1760
Brown, P., *Civil and Natural History of Jamaica*, 1756
Bry, T. de, *America*, 13 pts, Frankfurt 1590–1634
Buonanni, F., *Ricreatione*, Rome 1681;
  Musaeum Kircherianum, Rome 1709;
  Rerum Naturalia Historia, Rome 1773–82
Catesby, M., *Natural History of Carolina*, 1731–43
Charleton, W., *Onomasticon Zoicon*, 1668;
  2nd edn, *Exercitationes . . .*, 3 vols, Oxford 1677
Coïter, V., *Externarum et Internarum Principalum Humani Corporis*, Nuremberg 1573;
  Lectiones Gabrielis Fallopii, Nuremberg 1575
Collaert, A., *Avium Vivae Icones*, Antwerp [1610]
Collins, S., *A Systeme . . . Treating of the Body of Man, Beasts, Birds, Fish, &c.*, 2 vols, 1685
Creux, F. de, *Historia Canadensis*, Paris 1664
Descartes, R., *De Homine*, Leyden, 1664; French edn, Paris 1664
Dezallier d'Argenville, A. J., *L'Histoire Naturelle . . . la Lithologie et la Conchyliologie*, Paris
  1742; 2nd edn, 1755–7
Dilenius, J. J., *Historia Muscorum*, Oxford 1741; English edn, 1768
Dutfield, J., *A New and Complete Natural History of English Moths and Butterflies*, 1748–49
Edwards, G., *A Natural History of Birds*, 4 pts, 1743–51;
  Gleanings of Natural History, 3 pts, 1758–64;
  A Natural History of Uncommon Birds, 7 vols, 1743–51; the bibliography of these is
  confusing, but the last seems to be the sum of the first two.
Ellis, H., *A Voyage to Hudson's Bay*, 1748
Fabricius, H. F., *De Formatione Ovi*, Padua 1621;
  Tractatus quatuor, Frankfurt 1624
Frederick II of Hohenstaufen, *De Arte Venandi cum Avibus*, C. A. Wood and F. M. Fyfe
  (ed. and tr.), Stanford, California 1943
Germano, G., *Breve e Sustiale Trattato*, Naples 1625
Gesner (Gessner), C., *Historia Animalium*, 5 vols, Tiguri 1551–87;
  De Omne Rerum Fossilium Genere, Tiguri 1565
Grew, N., *Musaeum Regalis Societatis*, 1681
Gualtieri, N., *Index Testrum Conchylorum*, Florence 1742

Hennepin, L., *Nouvelle Decouverte d'un Très Grand Pays* [*Canada*], Utrecht 1697
Hernandez, F., *Rerum medicarum Novae Hispaniae Thesaurus*, Mexico 1615
Hill, J., *A General Natural History*, 3 vols 1748–52
Hooke, R., *Micrographia*, 1665;
   Posthumous Works, 1705;
   A Bibliography, by G. Keynes, Oxford 1960
Jonston, J., *Historia Naturalis de Quadrupedibus*, 4 vols, Frankfurt 1650–53;
   De Avibus, Amsterdam, 1657; new edns,
   Theatrum Universale, 1755–57,
   De Exanguibus Aquaticis, 1767,
   De Piscibus et Cetis, 1757,
   De Serpentibus, 1757, all published at Heilbronn.
Josselyn, J., *New England's Rarities Discovered*, 1672
Journal des Sçavans, 1 (1665)–
Kaempfer, E., *History of Japan*, 1727
Kircher, A., *Mundus Subterraneus*, Amsterdam 1664–65
Klein, J. T., *Descriptiones Tubulorum marinirum*, Gedani, 1731;
   Naturalis Dispositio Echinodermatum, Gedani 1734; French tr. 1754;
   Historiae Piscium, 5 pts, Gedani 1740–9;
   Historia Avium Prodromus, Lubeck 1750;
   Tentamen Methodi Ostracologicae, Leyden 1753
Knorr, G. W., *Sammlung von Merckwürdigkeiten der Natur und Ältherthümern des Erdbodens*, Nürnberg 1755;
   Die Naturgeschichte der Versteinerung, 2 vols, Nürnberg 1768
Laet, J. de, *Nieuwe Wereldt ofte Beschrijvinghe van West-Indien*, Leyden 1630
Lawson, J., *Allerneuste Beschreibung . . . Carolina*, Hamburg 1712
Liebniz, G. W., *Protagaea*, Göttingen 1749
Leeuwenhoek, A. van, *Ondervindingen en Beschouwingen . . .*, 4 pts, Leyden, 1684;
   Ontledingen en Ontdekkingen . . ., 5 pts, Leyden, 1685–86;
   Vervolg der Brieven, 6 pts, Leyden & Delft 1687–97;
   Leeuwenhoek and his 'Little Animals', by C. Dobell, 1932; reprint 1960
Leguat, F., *Voyage et Aventures*, 2 vols, Amsterdam 1708
Leigh, C., *The Natural History of Lancashire*, Oxford 1700
Le Page du Pratz, *Histoire de la Louisiane*, 3 vols, Paris 1758; English tr., 2 vols, 1763
Léry, J., *Histoire d'un Voyage Fait en la Terre du Brésil*, La Rochelle 1578
Lhwyd, E., *Lithophylacii Britannici Ichnographia*, 1699, 2nd edn 1760
Linnaeus, C., *Museum Tessinianum*, Stockholm 1753;
   Museum S. R. M. Adolphi Frederici, Stockholm 1754;
   Museum S. R. M. Ludovicae Ulricae Reginae, Stockholm 1764;
   A Catalogue of the Works of Linnaeus by B. B. Woodward, W. R. Wilson, and B. H. Soulsby, 2nd edn, 1933;
   The Compleat Naturalist by W. Blunt, 1971;
   Linnaeus and the Linneans, by F. A. Stafleu, Utrecht 1971;
   The Great Chain of Being, by A. O. Lovejoy, Cambridge, Mass. 1936
Lister, M., *Historia Animalium Angliae*, 1678;
   Johannes Godartius of Insects, 1682;
   Historiae Sive Synopsis Methodicae Conchylorum, 2 vols, 1685–97 — copies are very variable.
Maier, M., *Atalanta Fugiens*, Oppenheim 1617
Markham, G., *Maister-peece*, 1610;
   English Husbandman, 1613–15;

Hunger's Prevention, or the Art of Fowling, 1621

Merian, M. S., *Metamorphosis Insectorum Surinamensium*, Amsterdam 1705, new edn, extra plates, 1719;
  Histoire des Insects de l'Europe, Amsterdam 1730

Meyer, J. D., *Angenehmer und Nützlicher Zeit-Vertreib*, Nuremberg 1748–56

Mouffet, T., *Insectorum . . . Theatrum*, 1634; English tr. 1658, see under Topsell

Olaus Magnus, *Historia de Gentibus Septentrionalibus*, Rome 1555

Olina, G. P., *Uccelliera*, Rome 1622

Parkinson, J., *Paradisi in Sole Paradisus Terrestris*, 1629

Peacham, H., *Minerva Britanna*, 1612

Petiver, J., *Aquatilium Animalium Amboinae*, 1713;
  British Butterflies, 1717;
  Gazophylacium, 1702–06; new edn, 3 vols, 1764

Piso, W., and Marcgrave, G., *Historia Naturalis Brasiliae*, 2 vols, Leyden 1648;
  De Indiae, Amsterdam 1658

Plancus, J., (S. G. Bianchi), *De Conchis Minus Notis Liber*, Venice 1739

Plot, R., *The Natural History of Oxfordshire*, Oxford 1677;
  The Natural History of Staffordshire, Oxford 1686

Pluche, N. A., *Spectacle de la Nature*, 8 vols, Paris 1732–51

Ray, J., *Animalium Quadrupedum et Serpenti Generis*, 1693;
  Synopsis Methodica Avium et Piscium, 1713;
  Life and Works, by C. E. Raven, Cambridge 1942;
  A Bibliography, by G. Keynes, 1951; see also Willughby

Réaumur, R. A. F. de., *Mémoires pour Servir a l'Histoire à des Insectes*, 6 vols + atlas, Paris 1734–42;
  Pratique de l'Art de Faire Éclorre et d'Élever des Oiseaux, Paris 1751

Redi, F., *Esperienze Intorno Alla Generazione degl' Insetti*, Florence 1668

Regenfus, F. M., *Auserlesne Schnecken Muscheln und andre Schaal Thiere*, Copenhagen 1758

Rondelet, G., *Libri de Piscibus Marinis*, 2 vols, Leyden 1554–5

Royal Society; *Philosophical Transactions*, 1 (1665)–178 (1886); then series A and B from 179 (1887) on;
  Proceedings, 1 (1832)–, parts A and B from 75 (1905);
  Phil. Trans. abridged, 1665–1800, 19 vols, 1809;
  History, by T. Sprat, 1667;
  History, by T. Birch, 4 vols, 1756–57
  History of the Royal Society, by C. R. Weld, 1848;
  The Royal Society, by M. Purver, 1967;
  The Royal Society 1660–1940, by H. G. Lyons, Cambridge 1944

Rudbeck, O., *Fågelbok, 1693–1710*, B. Gullander (ed.), Stockholm 1971

Rumpf, G. E., *D'Amboinische Rareitkamer*, Amsterdam 1705; Latin tr. 1711 under the name Rumphius

Saccho, F. da T., *Opera di Mescalzia . . . de' Cavalli*, Rome 1591

Salviani, I., *Aquatilium Animalium Historiae*, Rome 1554

Seba, A., *Locupletissime Rerum Naturalium Thesauri*, 4 vols, Amsterdam 1734–65

Shaw, T., *Travels in Barbary and the Levant*, Oxford 1738

Sibbald, R., *Scotia Illustrata*, 3 vols, Edinburgh 1684

Sloane, H., *A Voyage to the Islands Madera, Barbados, Nieves, St. Christopher's, and Jamaica*, 2 vols, 1707–25;
  Sloane, by G. de Beer, 1953

Smith, C., *The Ancient and Present State of Waterford*, Dublin 1746

Smith, W., *A New Voyage to Guinea*, 1744

Snape, A., *The Anatomy of an Horse*, 1683

Steno, N., *Elementorum Myologiae Specimen*, Florence 1667;
  De Solido intra Solidum Prodromus, Florence 1669;
  The prodromus to a dissertation, Henry Oldenburg (tr.), 1671

Swammerdam, J., *Biblia Naturae*, H. Boerhaave (ed.), Leyden 1737; English tr. 1758

Topsell, E., *The Historie of Fore-footed beasts*, 1607;
  The Historie of serpents, 1608; new edn, with Mouffet's *Insects*, 3 vols, 1658

Trembley, A., *Mémoires*, Leyden 1744

Tyson, E., *Phoceana*, 1680;
  Orang-Outang, 1699

Valentijn, F., *Omstanding Verhaal van de Geschiedenissen . . . in Amboina*, Amsterdam 1724–26

Waldung, W., *Lagographia*, Ambergae 1619

White, J., *American Drawings*, P. H. Hulton and D. B. Quinn (eds.), 2 vols 1964;
  North American Birds, T. P. Harrison (ed.), Austin, Texas [1964]

Willughby, F., *Ornithologiae libri tres*, 1676; J. Ray (tr.), 1678;
  Historia Piscium, Oxford, 1686

Worm, O., *Historia animalis quod in Novagia . . .*, Hasniae, 1653;
  Museum Wormianium, Leyden 1655

4

The Great Age
of Illustrated Works

In 1768 Captain Cook set off in command of the *Endeavour*, bound for Tahiti, to make astronomical observations and then to seek the unknown southern continent, Terra Australis Incognita. On board he carried a zoological and a topographical artist, and also Joseph Banks and his friend Solander (a former pupil of Linnaeus) as naturalists, and Spöring (another Swede) as an assistant naturalist who also made drawings. The graphic records and the collections of specimens from this and Cook's later voyages were particularly splendid and full, but they were not unique in their kind. Linnaeus' students travelled all over the globe, sending back collections and descriptions to their relatively stay-at-home mentor; and after his death in 1778 they communicated with various eminent men of science such as Banks, and with scientific societies and academies.

Governments vied with one another in sending out expeditions to remote parts of the world, hoping to find new countries in which to establish settlements or with which to trade, and hoping to find new routes — such as a North-East or North-West Passage — to distant countries. Collectors went with these expeditions, sending back specimens to enrich the cabinets of the curious at home; and from the later eighteenth century a voyage came to seem the best way to make a career in the life sciences, even for those who already had a medical degree or some other professional qualification. A professional man might go on an expedition or embassy as naturalist, doctor, secretary, or chaplain; a keen gardener's boy, who had caught the eye of Banks in London or of Pallas in Russia, might go in the more humble role of collector, responsible for skinning the birds and drying or potting the plants. If he was successful,

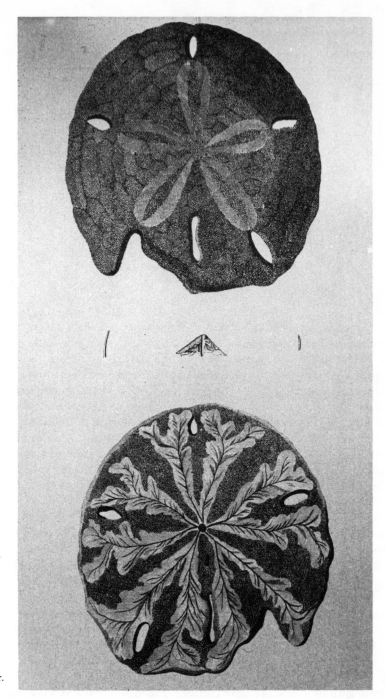

62
Sea urchins from North
West America, from La
Perouse's *Voyage* (English tr.
1799)

112

he might find himself duly launched upon an informal career structure involving a succession of jobs of higher status, as did George Caley and later John Gould.

On the other hand every expedition carried the risk of death, an obvious example being that of Sydney Parkinson the talented natural-history artist on Cook's first voyage, who died of a disease contracted at Batavia on the way home. His account of the voyage was published by his brother, who was engaged in a furious dispute with Banks over various alleged injustices; but because the natural history plates belonged to Banks, as Parkinson's employer, this book's illustrations are of ethnographical rather than zoological importance. Some zoological drawings were engraved for the official account of the voyage, edited by Hawksworth; but most remained unpublished, even though Banks had had copper plates engraved from them when the death of Solander in 1782 put a stop to the proposed publication. Cook's later voyages were written up by Cook himself, though that of his fatal last voyage had to be completed by Captain King, and these books contain some account of the natural history of the regions Cook visited. On the second voyage he was accompanied by George and Reinhold Forster as naturalists, the former of whom wrote an account of the voyage.

The emphasis in such works and others like *Uncommon Birds* of Edwards, was upon nondescripts — creatures never seen before, that must be named. Sometimes even though a collection might be described on publication as coming from one country, creatures from another, sometimes far distant, might be included because for one reason or another the author or artist had specimens or drawings to hand. The most notorious case of this is Sonnerat's *Voyage à la Nouvelle Guinée* of 1776; Sonnerat had never been there, but had assisted Commerson, the naturalist on Bougainville's circumnavigation of 1776–9, and at his death had appropriated his materials. The book thus included plates of a South American penguin and a Kookaburra (the latter deriving ultimately from Banks) which could not but confuse students of animal distribution.

The compiler at home had to rely upon the information supplied by the owner of the collection he studied, who relied upon whoever supplied it to him; and as the standards of labelling immediately on collecting were not as high in the eighteenth century as they later became, there was often uncertainty as to original location of a specimen. Most honest compilers duly reported such problems; Levaillant, for example, whose *Histoire Naturelle des Oiseaux d' Afrique*, *Histoire Naturelle des Oiseaux de Paradis*, and *Histoire Naturelle des Perroquets* are magnificently illustrated with plates (notably by Barraband — who had been trained as a designer of tapestries and porcelain) freely admitted that in the case of some specimens, such as the *Touraco Buffon*, that he was dependent on second-hand evidence of where ot had come from. His books, like those of his contemporary Latham, described birds from all over the world;

63   Plate by Barraband from Levaillant's *Perroquets* (1801–05)

114

64   Plate by Latham, from *The Voyage of Governor Phillip* (1789)

Latham's works in particular included birds from Australia, and he was often consulted by those who had voyaged to distant regions and were writing up their accounts; for example, in the standard history of the First Fleet to Botany Bay, *The Voyage of Governor Phillip*.

The exploration of Siberia, with reports upon its zoology, was a feature of the eighteenth century as the fur traders' knowledge was systematised and the country opened up. The famous expedition of Bering led to few written records; but Gmelin's expedition of 1733–43 resulted in a four-volume account which he published at Göttingen in 1751–2, and which proved extremely important for all branches of natural history. The party split up, and Kamchatka was separately described by Krasheninnikov, one of the few Russians who went on the expedition, as 'a student'; an English version was published in 1764. This book is valuable particularly because it contains zoological information derived from Steller, who first described the famous 'sea-cow'; he had accompanied Bering, but died in 1746 with his material, now lost, unpublished. The English version of the book uses Linnean names, the original Russian edition being post-Linnean in date (1755) but not in nomenclature.

The next major expedition to Siberia was under Pallas, and was contemporary with that of Cook and Banks to Tahiti, New Zealand and New South Wales. The voyage was described in his *Reise durch verschiedene Provinzen des Russischen Reichs* and *Spicilegia Zoologica*, both of which were illustrated with attractive plates of vertebrate and invertebrate animals, sometimes in their natural settings. After his return from Siberia, Pallas became adviser to the Empress Catherine on natural history and exploration, and was responsible for organising various voyages and land expeditions, including that of Billings into the Bering Straits, and the circumnavigation of Krusenstern with whom Langsdorff sailed and contributed to natural history in his *Voyages and Travels* of 1813. Pallas himself described further travels, to the Crimea, in a book published in 1799–1801; and he also edited works of Gmelin and of Steller on Siberia and its natural history.

Pallas was unhappy with the Linnean system, as was his correspondent Thomas Pennant, one of the best-known naturalists of his day in Britain and one of the recipients of the letters from Gilbert White that made up *The Natural History of Selborne*, 1789 (which contained one zoological plate, of the Stilt, and has had numerous later illustrated editions). Pennant acquired from Pallas much information for his *Arctic Zoology* of 1784–5, with a supplement in 1787; he also used specimens and descriptions supplied by Banks who had visited Labrador in 1766. Species familiar to 'Pennant and his readers, like the magpie, are described in addition to unfamiliar animals and birds; naturally, it is the latter which are illustrated, sometimes by famous artists — George Stubbs for example painted the moose, looking rather gloomily at its fallen antlers. The *Arctic Zoology* is then a genuine regional study, of the Palearctic

116

65
Gannet, from Pennant's
British Zoology (1776–77 edn)
—.an early action picture

and Nearctic regions; as such it was not superseded until the 1830's, when much
more information had been collected by travellers and explorers.

This was not Pennant's only regional study. His *British Zoology* went through
several editions after its first appearance in 1766, and was agreeably illustrated. The illustration showing the parts of birds — essentially a diagram —
also exemplifies the problems facing the eighteenth-century bookbinder; for it
is marked to be placed at page 140 of the quarto edition or page 160 of the
octavo. With its list of synonyms, its description, and its leisurely and anec-
dotal account of habits and habitats, Pennant's work is in the line of books, at
once scholarly and popular, on natural history that continues through the
nineteenth century in Britain, with authors such as William Yarrell. Occasionally Pennant is rather credulous in his use of anecdote: thus he has
squirrels going on rafts across rivers using their tails as sails, like Squirrel

Nutkin — but this was a story to which Linnaeus also gave currency, and so Pennant was in good company; it is now acknowledged that animal behaviour is so complex that the naturalist should not be too speedy in writing off vulgar errors.

The *Arctic Zoology* was originally intended to be an account of the zoology of the British colonies in North America. This area was less well known than Siberia, for the first man to reach the Arctic Ocean was Hearne in his journey of 1769–72 and the first to cross the continent was Mackenzie in 1792–3. But in 1776 came American independence, and the book took a different course — particularly with Pallas' contributions. There followed a brief period of post-imperial gloom and cynicism, which soon gave way with the planting of the settlement at Botany Bay in Australia, and the consolidation of the Indian dominions of the East India Company. Pennant had already brought out a work on *Indian Zoology* (in 1769) illustrated with twelve coloured plates; another edition, augmented by Forster, was produced in 1790. The latter was essentially an essay towards an Indian zoology, for as yet little was systematically known of the fauna of the oriental region; it was not until the mid nineteenth century that Indian zoology began to receive the full and detailed treatment that European countries had long been enjoying, with due attention to creatures found also in Europe as well as to exotic ones.

Pennant did not describe Arctic invertebrates, although travellers did not fail to mention the mosquitoes; but he had dealt with British ones. Butterflies have always been almost as popular as birds for natural history subjects, and in the late eighteenth century there were many splendid illustrated works, from the brilliantly — indeed almost garishly — coloured pictures in Wilkes' *120 Copper plates* (1773) to the delicacy of Lewin's *Insects* or *Papilios* (1795); both works showed the caterpillar and the chrysalis as well as the adult, but Wilkes' insects are portrayed on the plants they frequent. The same is true of the butterflies in J. E. Smith's *Rarer Lepidopterous Insects of Georgia* (1797), which is perhaps the most magnificent butterfly book ever produced. Other students of butterflies included Moses Harris, whose book *The Aurelian* (1766) has a frontispiece of butterfly collectors with their nets (an aurelian was Harris' term for a lepidopterist), and handsome plates separately dedicated and each bearing a coat of arms. Harris also wrote a more general book on English insects, and did the plates for the *Illustrations of Natural History* of Drury, the well-known collector of insects who also wrote an *Exotic Entomology*.

The botanist William Curtis was interested in entomology, and indeed published a short monograph on the 'brown-tail moth' (*Euproctis chrysorrhoea* Linn.) in 1782 when there was a population explosion of these creatures to the extent that they were a pest to gardeners. Curtis's is an early example of this kind of economic zoology, and is illustrated with a handsome plate; just as hunting has led to zoological knowledge among the higher groups, so in entomology the desire to control vermin has been a stimulus to science —

118

perverse though this seems in both cases. Curtis was a friend of A. H. Haworth who lived near him in Chelsea, and to whom he gave his collections of insects. Haworth published his *Lepidoptera Britannica* in three parts from 1803 to 1812, in octavo; it was systematic in a way its predecessors had not been. In the previous year, Haworth had published anonymously a *Prodromus*, listing British species of butterflies but without illustrations; and had founded the Aurelian Society, whose members were to contribute a specimen to the collection upon joining. The society never reached a membership of twenty; and in 1806 Haworth was a leading founder-member of the Entomological Society of London — which again did not prosper as an independent body, and was absorbed later by the Linnean Society.

Haworth's collections, including over a thousand butterflies among some forty thousand insects, were catalogued after his death by J. O. Westwood, whom we shall meet again later; many of the specimens passed to the British Museum which by the 1830s was beginnning to become a worthy national collection. In 1818 J. F. Stephens, at the request of the trustees of the British Museum, was granted leave from his office at the Admiralty to help in arranging the collections of insects; as a result of this work he became an authority on entomology, and published *Illustrations of British Entomology* from 1827 to 1837, with a supplement in 1846, as well as a *Systematic Catalogue* in 1829. On his retirement in 1845 Stephens returned to the Museum and catalogued the lepidoptera. Contemporary with Stephens' *Illustrations* was the *British Entomology* (8 vols, 1824–39) of John Curtis, with very careful and exact illustrations by the author (who was no relation of the William Curtis mentioned previously). He was a friend of J. C. Dale, an important early entomologist, and of Leach, who was keeper of zoology in the British Museum; his book, despite attacks on parts of it by Stephens, was highly praised by Cuvier. Curtis was later consulted about fossil insects by Murchison and Lyell; and his earliest work had been illustrations for the *Introduction to Entomology* of Kirby and Spence.

The *Introduction*, which came out in four volumes, began like other popular works of the time in the form of letters, urging the importance, interest and dignity of the science; but the later volumes are more severe and like a textbook, though still written in an easy and untechnical way. It was a very successful work, going through a number of editions; and Kirby became one of the most eminent entomologists of his day, writing up the insects collected on various voyages, and contributing in 1837 the volume on entomology to Richardson's *Fauna Boreali-Americana*. By then he was in his seventy-eighth year; but his old age had been thoroughly active, because in 1835 he had published one of the Bridgewater Treatises on the existence and goodness of God, demonstrated in Kirby's volume from the 'History, Habits and Instincts of Animals'. His volumes were part of a famous series, but the preoccupation with studying nature in order to learn about God was characteristic of Kirby,

66
Various insects, from Kirby
and Spence, *Introduction to
Entomology* (1822 edn)

120

67
Lepidoptera, from Priscilla Wakefield's *Introduction to Entomology* (1815); an elementary work in the form of letters.

who was a country clergyman; and was indeed characteristic of many natural historians of his time in Britain.

Kirby and Spence did not found entomology in Britain, and from the time of Linnaeus we find various works, of a more or less systematic character. Botany and entomology seem to have frequently gone together at this period; William Curtis we have already noticed, Haworth was a distinguished botanist, Kirby made himself known as a botanist before writing about insects; but Thomas Martyn, Professor of Botany at Cambridge, is not to be confused with the contemporary of the same name who produced in 1792 his *English Entomologist*. This is illustrated with plates of beetles, drawn by pupils at Martyn's academy for drawing and printing natural history in London; and very splendid some of them are. In 1797 he published (apparently in an edition of only ten copies) *Psyche*, a work on the lepidoptera with ninety-six figures on thirty-two plates, and descriptions in manuscript. As well as works on insects, Martyn produced a new edition of Albin's work on spiders, and a very handsome book on shells, *The Universal Conchologist*, for which he received medals from various potentates abroad. The text of this work, as of a number of other works of natural history at the time, was in both English and French.

Among such dual-language books was Barbut's *Genera Vermium*, which followed his *Genera Insectorum of Linnaeus* of 1780. On the frontispiece of the former work appears a quotation from Pliny: 'While I contemplated Nature, She wrought in me a Persuasion, that I should look upon nothing as incredible that related to her.' The 'worms' of Linnaeus were indeed a surprising group, into which little order was brought until Lamarck published his *Animaux sans Vertébrés*, 1801. The invertebrates were difficult to draw because of their lack of definite form and because the functions of their organs and their relationships were not understood — and one cannot draw what one does not understand. Barbut's illustrations, which include intestinal worms, slugs, and starfishes are nevertheless very handsome, and his descriptions were based upon dissections.

It was not only in Britain and in France that illustrated works of natural history were published in the late eighteenth and early nineteenth centuries, as we can see from the lists of books given by Cuvier in his *Rapport Historique* of 1810, pp. 283ff. Despite its excessive praise of Napoleon (to whom it is addressed) it is a useful work whose bias only extends as far as emphasising French contributions to the field, without neglecting or disparaging works from other countries. Indeed, at this time the French were dominant across a whole range of sciences, and could afford to be generous; the loss of French hegemony is one of the features of the history of science in the nineteenth century. In Italy Spallanzani's researches refuting the notion of spontaneous generation among micro-organisms became well known, though not universally accepted; in Germany Fabricius produced various systematic works on entomology from 1775, and Panzer published plates of insects; and in Switzerland Clairville produced his *Entomologie Helvétique* (Zurich, 1798) with text in

68   Scarabs, from Martyn's *English Entomologist* (1792)

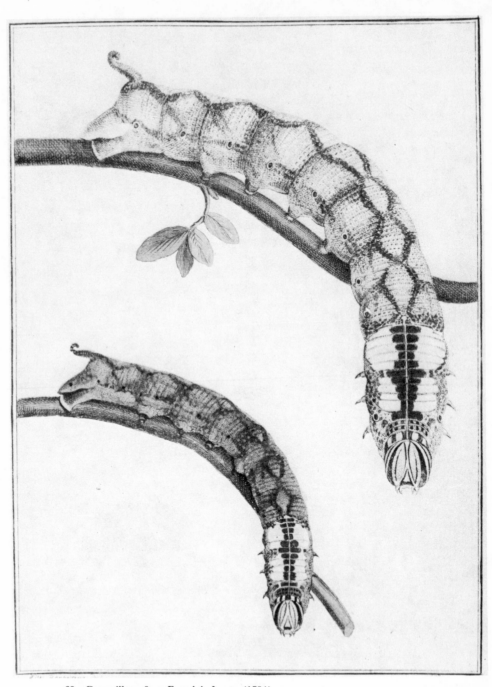

69   Caterpillars, from Fuessly's *Insectes* (1794)

124

French and German, and Fuessly his *Histoire des Insectes* (Winterthur, 1794).

There were thus among works on invertebrates technical and systematic writings, such as those of Lamarck; experimental and microscopic works such as those of Spallanzani; regional studies, such as that of Clairville; and collections of exotics, like Cramer's *Papillons Exotiques* of 1779–90. The first and probably the second of these classes were for serious students of the science, and by 1800 a group of such people was beginning to emerge as specialisation went on apace; although as we saw in England attempts to found entomological societies in the first decade of the nineteenth century did not prosper. The third and fourth group could appeal to laymen and also provide genuine and important contributions to science; but as time went on the collection and description of 'non-descripts' became of less importance, while the study of animal distribution, and therefore of regional works, became increasingly important. Both these groups contain splendidly illustrated works; for in the late eighteenth and early nineteenth centuries, there were wealthy landowners who were prepared to subscribe not only to works of picturesque scenery but also to expensive works of natural history; and because natural history was thus fashionable, they were joined by manufacturers and merchants. One of the effects of the industrial and agricultural revolutions in Britain was that they made possible the sale, and therefore the publication, of very handsome and costly books; for France, we need a different explanation — probably the munificence of Napoleon's government in matters of science.

Barbut's *Genera Vermium* included sea-urchins, of which he described and illustrated a number of living forms; and the late eighteenth century saw also a number of attractively-illustrated works on conchology — shells have always lent themselves as attractive subjects both for collection and illustration. Shells, and the remains of sea-urchins, are also objects commonly found as fossils; by 1800 it had become at last generally accepted that fossil forms, with their tantalising resemblances to and differences from existing species, were in fact the remains of creatures. It was still necessary for James Parkinson, the surgeon who described 'Parkinson's Disease', to urge this point in the first volume of his *Organic Remains of a Former World*, 1804; like Kirby and Spence's, this book began in the form of letters, but the last volume (1811), heavily leaning on Cuvier and Lamarck, became something more like a textbook. Parkinson had been a radical in his youth, and was even suspected of having had some part in a plot to assassinate King George III; but by the time he wrote this book his opinions seem to have become more conservative. The frontispiece consists of a rocky coastline with Noah's Ark aground in the distance at the rainbow's end, and on the beach in the foreground lie the shells of ammonites and belemnites. The message thus implied is that extinct creatures are those which failed to get a passage in the Ark; even in 1804 it was a difficult proposition to accept for anybody who had noticed that the extinct

70
The donkey; a more
picturesque creature than
the horse; from Gilpin's
Forest Scenery (1794 edn)

creatures in the various strata are not all the same. But few had made such an
observation, because those interested in fossils had been concerned with their
origins or simply with classifying them; while geologists like Werner, had been
chiefly concerned with mineralogy, or sometimes with wide-ranging specula-
tions about the origin of the Earth.

It was the canal surveyor William Smith who first realised the value of the
study of fossils for determining the order in which the strata had been laid
down; his conclusions had become known in Britain during the early years of
the nineteenth century, but his map and argument were not published until
1815. His discoveries were at once taken up by others, whilst Smith himself
lived on in relative obscurity till his death in 1839. Subsequently he underwent
an odd 'resurrection' when King Louis Phillippe was smuggled out of France
after the 1848 Revolution in the guise of 'William Smith, geologist'; a scheme
masterminded by Featherstonehaugh the British Consul at Le Havre.

Before Smith's ideas were published, Cuvier in France had come to similar

71   Frontispiece to Parkinson's *Organic Remains*, I (1811 edn)

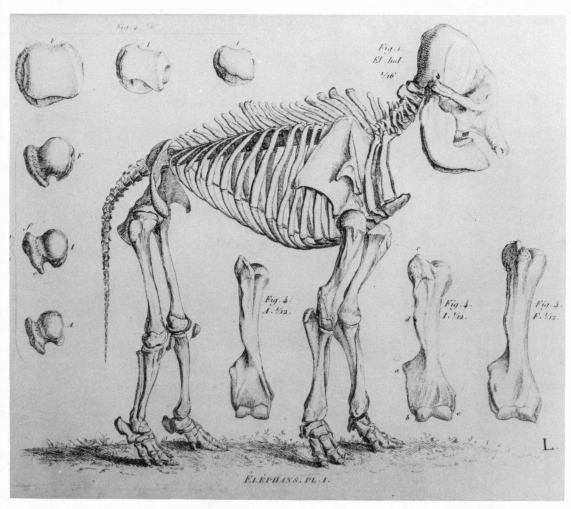

72
Elephant skeleton, from
Cuvier's *Ossemens fossiles*
(1821–24 edn)

conclusions as a result of studying the tertiary fossils of the Paris Basin, thrown up with the stone which was being quarried in order to build Paris anew as an imperial capital under Napoleon. To interpret the jumbled fossil bones that had been found, Cuvier had recourse to what he called the principle of correlation, which amounted to a reiteration of the idea that the parts of animals all cohere together in a general plan. The leg bones of a creature with cloven hoofs cannot be compatible with a skull containing well-developed canine teeth, for the former are characteristic of a herbivore and the latter of a carnivore. To separate, as Cuvier did, various species of extinct rhinoceros demanded great experience in comparative anatomy; and to have studied zoology became a necessity for the geologist, with mineralogy virtually abandoned to chemists. In the Museum of Natural History in Paris Cuvier built up such collections of fossils and of zoological specimens that during the first thirty years of the century it was the most important centre for zoological and palaeontological research in the world.

Cuvier's work was based upon the idea that species could be unambiguously determined from bones, and thus had constant characters. Any bone — recent or fossil — must come from some species of creature, either previously described or new; not surprisingly the hypothesis of his colleague Lamarck, that species might be transformed over long periods of time so that nature was always in flux, was anathema to Cuvier; moreover it seemed to be refuted by his work, for he rarely found missing links that were ambiguous, and he showed that cats mummified in Egypt two thousand years before did not differ from nineteenth-century cats in France. Cuvier accounted for the different populations of the different strata by a theory of catastrophes, global or local, which had swept away one set of creatures leaving the way clear for a new set to be created or to immigrate from elsewhere. Extinction — unless caused by man, as with the dodo — was a phenomenon associated with catastrophes rather than something happening in the ordinary course of nature.

The work of Cuvier and of Smith brought the palaeontologist — an Ezekiel calling dry bones to life — into prominence even outside the scientific community, and helped to make geology the most exciting science of the early nineteenth century. The illustration of fossils became an important part of zoological illustration; and as with zoological illustration, attention shifted from exotic and attractive specimens to the study of a whole population, for in using fossils to determine the geological period of a stratum it was not merely a few dramatic specimens that were important but rather the whole aspect of the population. Careful illustrations of typical fossils were needed; but these, on the whole, came later than 1830. In the heroic early days, works such as Parkinson's were illustrated with beautifully engraved and coloured plates of curious fossils such as the stone lily (remains of stalked starfish); while the bones in Cuvier's *Recherches sur les Ossemens Fossiles*, in Mantell's *Fossils of the South Downs* (1822) and in Buckland's *Reliquiae Diluvianae* (1823), are again magnificent examples of anatomical illustration.

Some of Buckland's plates, as we remarked before, were engraved because they had been made for the paper published by the Royal Society in which he described the Kirkdale Cavern where he had seen what seemed to him evidence of Noah's Flood; while other illustrations done for the book, were printed by the newer and cheaper process of lithography. Lithography was also used by J. S. Miller in his very attractively-illustrated *Natural History of the Crinoidea*, 1821, in which he went beyond Parkinson in discussion of the stone-lilies and which included exploded drawings to show how the various parts had fitted together. Crinoid ossicles, from the stalk of the starfish, had puzzled naturalists since Gesner; and it was not until the late eighteenth

129

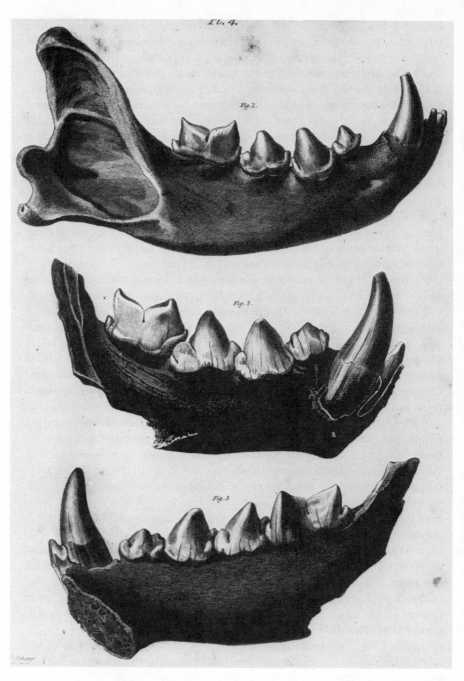

73   Jaws of recent and extinct hyænas, from Buckland's *Reliquiae Dilwianae* (1823)

130

century that a living form was found in deep water off the West Indies, and not until 1823 that J. V. Thompson discovered a European form at Cork (a mere three-quarters of an inch long) so that for the first time a living crinoid could be studied by a competent observer. Thompson found to his surprise, and that of his contemporaries, that this stalked creature was the juvenile form of the feather-star. In the study of this group, therefore, zoology and palaeontology went hand in hand; Thompson indeed published his *Memoir* (1827) in quarto format, with an illustration, so that it could be bound in with Miller's book. From 1828 he published a series of *Zoological Researches and Illustrations*, illuminating for the first time the life-cycle of the crab and the barnacle.

Starfish had been described and depicted by Barbut, who had separated them into 'intire', 'stellated', and 'radiated' kinds. In his introduction Barbut wrote of the way that 'the full complement of every genus, is kept up to compleat every link in the chain of nature', alluding to the notion that there was a Great Chain of Being reaching up from the lowliest living being (or indeed from minerals) to man and perhaps on to angels. The idea that this chain existed was seriously weakened as evidence accumulated that creatures had become extinct, for it was essentially a timeless system; and the argument was further assailed on other grounds, the most notable being Cuvier's insistence that it was impossible to arrange even the animal kingdom as a continuous series. Cuvier eventually settled upon four great groups: Vertebrata, Mollusca, Articulata, and Radiata, the last group including *inter alia* all the various kinds of starfish — the least convincing of Cuvier's *embranchements*. The chain or ladder of creation had therefore given way to a tree; and in giving up the old theory, any idea of development which involved a steady climbing of the old ladder had to be given up too. In Cuvier's system, the starfish, the crab, and the bullhead that we see in a rock pool all belong to distinct series rather than being links on one chain; only the starfish and the sea anemone would be placed in a common province.

At first Cuvier's system had possessed some symmetry and elegance, each of the four provinces being subdivided into four groups; but he soon found, as his predecessors had, that such a scheme cannot be made to work, and the classification in his great zoological compendium, *La Règne Animal* (1816) lacks formal harmony of this kind, though the four basic divisions remained and were generally accepted in the first half of the nineteenth century as the basic taxonomic groups. Cuvier had been working on this *magnum opus* since he had begun to be interested in zoology more than twenty years before; the insects, however, were written up by Latreille, who held another chair at the Museum. The book formed the greatest body of zoological facts ever put together and remained for a generation a standard work; it had two editions in Cuvier's lifetime, and was translated into various languages. The translation into English by Griffith and others, which appeared between 1827 and 1835 in sixteen volumes, is very good, being brought up to date where it was necessary.

The book was well-illustrated, and is an excellent guide to the state of zoological knowledge at that time.

Cuvier's important work on mammalian fossils (published in 1812 and
broadened in scope by editions in 1821–4 and 1825) was more original; but his
great innovatory work in zoology was on fishes, produced (in eight volumes
between 1828 and 1833) in conjunction with Valenciennes who subsequently
carried the work further, alone. Previously Peter Artedi had begun to sys-
tematise the science of ichthyology; after his early death in 1734 his papers had
passed to his fellow-student Linnaeus who edited them, making some
modifications and additions, though these changes were small enough in
Günther's opinion to entitle Artedi to be called the 'Father of Ichthyology'.
Gronow, a German living in Holland, devised the method of preparing flat
dried skins of fish so that they could be preserved rather like plants in an
herbarium; he published two books on fish, *Museum Ichthyologicum*, 1754–6, and
Zoophylacium, 1763–81; and J. E. Gray edited and published in 1854 his *Systema
Ichthyologicum* which he had not himself got into print at the time of his death.

The next great student of fish was Mark Bloch, a physician in Berlin, who
published his first work on them when he was fifty-six. His work on German
fish came out between 1782 and 1784, and that on foreign fish from 1785 to

1795, the text being in quarto, with folio atlases of plates. Bloch had resolved to give full descriptions of every species known to him, and to illustrate them with excellent drawings; as a result his work is one of the most sumptuous ever produced. At his time it was still possible to contemplate undertaking a work of this magnitude; by the nineteenth century there were too many species known. Bloch's German fishes, all described and depicted from nature, were still (according to Günther) serviceable a century later, many still being the best existing in the literature; but for the foreign fishes he could not avoid all the pitfalls that await anyone who has perforce to work from drawings and descriptions given by travellers of various degrees of ichthyological competence, and from specimens of doubtful provenance.

Bloch's contemporary Lacépède, who completed Buffon's great work and was a colleague of Cuvier at the Museum in Paris, published the next important general study of fish, his *Histoire des Poissons* appearing in Paris between 1798 and 1803. This book was compiled under difficulties owing to the political situation in France in the 1790s, and therefore was not free from errors; for the author often had to rely on notes rather than on collections and books. Lacépède's illustrations are less magnificent than those of Bloch; but nevertheless his book was a great achievement and was for a quarter of a century the standard work. During this period there were regional works on fish that are noteworthy, including two from India, where in geography, botany and zoology soldiers and officials of the East India Company were making important contributions to science in what was to become an important tradition. Russell's *Two Hundred Fishes Collected at Vizagapatam* (1803) and Hamilton's *Fishes Found in the River Ganges* (1822) both had excellent and very accurate illustrations; both authors were medical men. It was Russell who had induced the Company to request medical officers to collect data of natural history, and to publish natural history; one of the early works published thus was Russell's own *Account of Indian Serpents* (1796–1809 — the last parts appearing after his death) for like Lacépède he was a devotee of herpetology as well as ichthyology. Nearer the great metropolitan centres of science, the fish of the Mediterranean were described by A. Risso in his *Ichthyologie de Nice*, 1810.

These various works formed the foundation for the tomes of Cuvier and Valenciennes, who indeed reviewed the history of the science at the beginning of their *Histoire Naturelle des Poissons*. Making use of the unrivalled collections at the Museum, many of their descriptions were masterly and their critical reviews of the literature discerning; but apparently like Homer, Cuvier occasionally made mistakes through lack of attention, particularly later, and some of the descriptions are insufficiently precise to satisfy his successors or to measure up to his own highest standards. After Cuvier's death, Valenciennes — who had been his pupil before becoming his collaborator — carried on the work until 1848, but it was never completed, some groups being still left

CRESTED BLACK WATER-CHAT

75
Plate from Swainson's
Flycatchers (1838), vol. 13 of
Jardine's *Naturalists' Library*.

undescribed. There were various editions; Günther says that the one chiefly used by ichthyologists was the octavo, with either plain or coloured plates, which apparently had the same text as the quarto edition but a different pagination — this last being the more luxurious version. Cuvier's system, based upon comparative anatomy and the use of a wide range of characters, became the basis for the classification of fish through the nineteenth century; and as one might expect, he incorporated fossil fish into the scheme along with living species.

As well as the Museum with its great collections and library — and Cuvier's prestige ensured that fresh consignments of specimens kept coming to the Museum from collectors — he had on the same site a zoological garden; this can still be visited, and some of the buildings go back to Cuvier's time. Some of the animals there had come from the menageries assembled by noblemen and by the king in pre-revolutionary times; for the zoologists at the Museum they provided an opportunity of studying exotic creatures alive and in 1801 Cuvier and Lacépède published an illustrated catalogue of the menagerie. Zoos, like museums, have always had the double function of advancing science and of entertaining and interesting visitors whose curiosity is more desultory. In 1826 the Zoological Society of London was set up, the chief movers being Raffles, who had recently returned to Europe after founding Singapore, and Davy, President of the Royal Society, who was concerned that Britain should have an institution comparable to Cuvier's Museum. Raffles seems to have been more interested in the advance of zoology as a pure science; while Davy, who at the Royal Institution had played the part of the apostle of applied science to the landed gentry, was keener on the acclimatisation of potentially-useful animals — but both agreed that the Society should have a zoo.

Zoological illustration can be more accurate and lively when the animal can be seen in the zoo rather than reconstructed from skin and bones and rough sketches. In 1830–1, there appeared under the editorship of E. T. Bennett *The Gardens and Menagerie of the Zoological Society Delineated*, containing woodcuts of well over one hundred animals and birds in the zoo; one of them, of a toucan roosting, depicts behaviour which could not have been worked out from a dead bird or at all easily observed in the wild.

Bennett's work also contained remarks about, though it did not illustrate, the Malay tapir; which was first described and illustrated in the West by Horsfield (a protégé of Raffles) in his *Zoological Researches in Java* (1824). A specimen subsequently confined in the menagerie of the Governor-General of India at Barrackpore was seen by a French zoologist, whose countrymen credited him with discovering it, to the fury of Bennett. The cudgels were taken up by Swainson on behalf of the French in the *Magazine of Natural History*; he was having a row with Bennett who, as secretary of the Zoological Society, would not let him — a Member of the Society who had resigned — use the collections he wanted to see in describing the birds for the *Fauna Boreali-*

Americana. Swainson by way of contrast had been made welcome at French institutions; he rushed into one of those furious public quarrels which were a feature of science in nineteenth-century Britain. When in 1812 the young Faraday asked Davy to help him devote himself to science, Davy smiled at his 'notion of the superior moral feelings of philosophic men', and added that the experience of a few years would set him right on that matter.

Horsfield's was not the only regional study to appear at this time, for travellers to distant regions wrote up accounts of what they had seen. The greatest work in this genre was that of Humboldt, who described all aspects of those parts of South and Central America he had visited on his famous expedition of 1799–1804, with Bonpland. His work was published between 1805 and 1832, the section on zoology being contained in two volumes with fifty-seven plates. Humboldt's struggles to publish his work in a fitting — that is, a magnificent — manner are well-known, and were ultimately successful,

76
The Anjing-ayer, by a
Chinese artist, from
Marsden's *Sumatra* (1811
edn)

136

77 Wild turkeys, from Wilson's *American Ornithology* (1831 edn)

although in thus erecting a monument to himself and to the engravers and printers of Paris he spent his entire fortune. In Paris he had the resources of the Museum behind him, and he remained there despite Napoleon's distaste for having an enemy alien thus working away in Paris. We can remember that Davy similarly was allowed to come to Paris to collect his prize for work in electrochemistry, although he was no francophile; science was still sometimes above politics.

In 1808 Alexander Wilson began publication of his *American Ornithology*, which eventually appeared in nine quarto volumes down to 1814. It was printed, and the illustrations engraved, in Philadelphia. Following the example of Catesby, Wilson had tried to teach himself engraving; he found that the results were much weaker than his drawing had been, and therefore commissioned Alexander Lawson to do them — which he could afford, because he had the backing of Samuel Bradford, a publisher, who had already given him a job preparing the American edition of *Rees' Cyclopedia*. Wilson took his systematic information from Latham's *General Synopsis of Birds*, and from the writings of George Edwards, but the work was not systematically organised. Some of Wilson's plates were very fine, though it is odd to occasionally see on the same plate quite unrelated birds that do not share a habitat; some are systematic, and others ecological (showing habitat), but many look like the worked-up pages of a sketchbook. It is a pity that Wilson's book is less well-known than those of some predecessors and successors — notably Audubon — for he was in fact the founder of American ornithology, and his plates are both decorative and of scientific importance.

In 1824–8, there was a second edition in three volumes of Wilson's book, at Philadelphia; and meanwhile that useful member of an illustrious family, Lucien Bonaparte, Prince of Musignano, had begun to publish his *American Ornithology* (1825–8) as a supplement to Wilson's — this was also illustrated with coloured plates, and in quarto format. His formal zoological knowledge was greater than Wilson's and he improved on the nomenclature and arrangement of Wilson's work. Thus when European editions of Wilson's work were published they were based upon the work of both Wilson and Bonaparte. Jameson's edition, appropriately published in Scotland (Wilson's native land), came out in four small volumes, unillustrated (except for frontispiece vignettes), in 1831; while in the following year an edition by Jardine appeared in three octavo volumes, with coloured illustrations. In 1831 Captain Thomas Brown, who seems to have been given to trespassing on other people's territory, brought out his *Illustrations of American Ornithology* compiled from the work of Wilson and Bonaparte; some of his illustrations are very fine, but as Dr Lysaght has pointed out he was sometimes unfortunate, as when he depicted a snowy owl in a southern magnolia tree — the sort of accident that may befall a compiler.

The name Audubon is familiar to everybody regardless of whether they

138

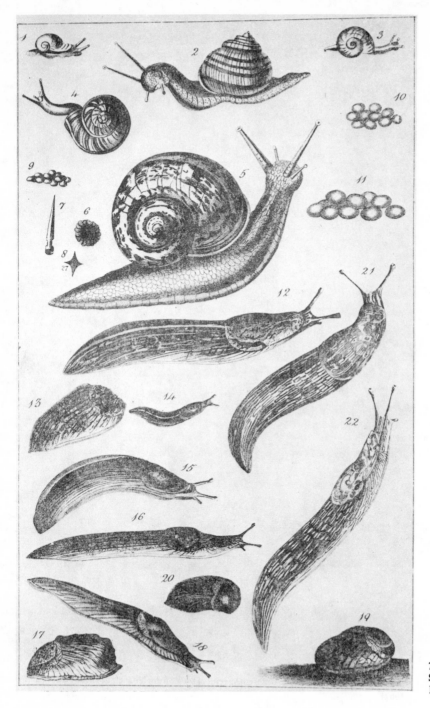

78
Slugs and snails, from
Brown's *British Shells* (1845)

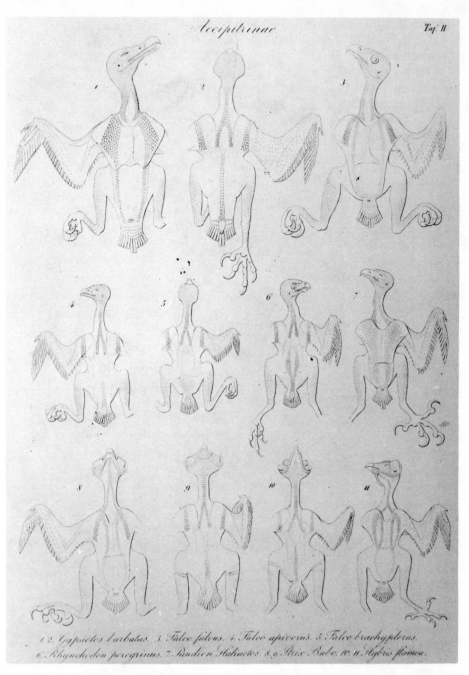

79 Disposition of feathers in different species of birds; from Nitzsch's *Pterylography* (English edn, 1867)

know anything else about natural history illustration; any new zoological artist is compared to him in popular reviews, and selections from his plates are reprinted in numerous editions. Audubon was a skilled self-advertiser and promoted his own work most successfully, so that his fame eclipsed that of his predecessors. Natural historians have never been so ecstatic about his work as have the general public; for he was not a trained zoologist, and therefore did not know as much as would have been desirable about the anatomy of birds, or the way the feathers are differently arranged in different species. This last point was brought home to men of science by C. L. Nitzsch, whose work on pterlyography remained mostly unpublished until 1840, after his death; while from 1804 to 1806 Stubbs had brought out his *Comparative Anatomical Exposition of the Human Body, the Tiger and the Common Fowl*. Audubon was criticised in his own day, and has been since, for displaying his birds sometimes in extravagant and unnatural attitudes, partly because of his ignorance of anatomy; but in some cases subsequent study has shown that he was right and the 'closet' naturalists who criticised him were wrong.

This having been said, it must be admitted that Audubon's plates are breathtaking and never dull. The great plates of double-elephant size — making the book about a metre high — are magnificent, and seemed to give Europeans and Americans from the Eastern seaboard a glimpse of the really wild west in the days before the cowboys. The plates were prepared on this scale so that as far as possible the birds could be shown as large as life; and much is lost when they are reduced in size, as for convenience they have to be to fit into ordinary books at ordinary prices. This is true of the work of any artist who has worked on a big scale, for he has expected his work to be seen full-size and had indeed chosen to do the picture of a certain size for certain reasons; but among natural-history illustrators, Audubon's use of so large a scale is unique. In his own lifetime, an edition reduced in size was prepared, and is of course more common than the original edition of 1827–38. The latter was engraved and coloured under Audubon's supervision by the Havells in London and only two hundred sets were printed, selling at one thousand dollars a set — enough to make even Nathan Rothschild think twice before buying one.

The descriptions of the birds were published in *Ornithological Biography*, which appeared in five volumes in Edinburgh from 1831 to 1839; the technical part was written by William Macgillivray, one of the most gifted of ornithologists. On almost as big a scale as Audubon's were the volumes of Prideaux Selby's *Illustrations of British Ornithology*, the plates of which began to appear in 1821, with two volumes of text in 1825 and 1833 — the whole work being complete by 1834, with 228 plates, some of them engraved as well as drawn by Selby, and showing the birds life-size. Selby also collaborated with Jardine in *Illustrations of Ornithology*, four quarto volumes 1825–43, and wrote the text for the volumes in Jardine's well-known *Naturalists' Library* on parrots

80
Little Egret, from Selby's
British Ornithology (1821–34)

and pigeons, which were illustrated by Edward Lear — thus playing a part in producing some of the largest and smallest bird books of his time. Lear's illustrations, like those in Nozeman's beautiful *Nederlandsche Vogelen* of 1770–1829, are less dramatic and romantic than those of Audubon, but are none the worse for that. The same could be said for Lesson's humming birds, and the birds illustrated in Vieillot's *Histoire Naturelle des Oiseaux de l'Amerique Septentrionale*, 1807; Vieillot recorded bird behaviour and studied variations of plumage with age rather than simply painting a dead specimen, but his plates were accurate rather than lively.

A field in which illustrations are required to be accurate rather than lively is anatomical art; and there were some splendid examples produced during this period. One of the most distinguished of the anatomists and physiologists was Charles Bell, who in 1798 while still a student in Edinburgh published his *System of Dissections*, and in 1804 published with his brother John an *Anatomy of the Human Body*. Bell then came to London, and in 1806 published his *Essays on the Anatomy of Expression in Painting*, which became very famous; Benjamin West, President of the Royal Academy, had advised the publishers to accept it;

142

the book explains how the muscles of the face work, and has striking illustrations. Bell's book appeared in a seventh edition in 1900, and was thus important throughout the nineteenth century; he considered that because men were susceptible to emotions and sympathies unknown to the lower animals, they were supplied with muscles — such as those that move the eyebrows and the corners of the mouth — to express them. This difference between men and animals was later combatted by Darwin, in his *Expression of the Emotions* (1872), who argued for a continuum, showing that in different animals different muscles appeared in different stages of development — Darwin's book is strikingly illustrated too, being one of the earliest scientific treatises to contain photographs.

Bell was a formidable figure, whom Darwin needed to take on even thirty years after his death, because of his work on the nervous system. He distinguished the two kinds of nerve endings that go with sensory and motor functions, first publishing his findings in a short essay of 1811, and finally fully writing up his work in the *The Nervous System of the Human Body* in 1830. Bell had

81
Humming bird, from
Lesson's *Oiseaux-mouches*
(1831)

been involved in a priority dispute with Magendie; but it seems certain that Bell was first, though his demonstration took longer because he would not do the vivisections practised by the Frenchman. He wrote, and it should be counted to his credit: 'I cannot perfectly convince myself that I am authorised in nature or religion to do these cruelties.' In 1833 Bell duly published a Bridgewater Treatise on the existence and benevolence of God as exemplified in the design of the human hand; this book too was illustrated from Bell's drawings.

The book on the nervous system that made Bell's reputation was based upon papers that had appeared through the 1820s in the Royal Society's *Philosophical Transactions*. This sequence of publication was a normal pattern by the early nineteenth century, as it still is today: the papers assure a man's priority, and bring work to the attention of his contemporaries rapidly; and when the course of research is completed, they can be rewritten into a book. In the later nineteenth century, the papers of eminent men of science were often collected and published, in their lifetime or perhaps posthumously; such collections are sometimes monuments of filial piety, embalming work that was no longer of interest to anybody active in the science. In the early nineteenth century such practices did not usually occur, and papers were to some extent reworked into a book and published when they were still fresh. Papers published in a journal at that time were often less generally available than was a book; scientific societies exchanged their publications, and of course issued them to members, but papers could easily be missed, especially by those in other countries, and the great Reviews of the day discussed important books at length but only infrequently wrote up an issue of a journal.

The *Philosophical Transactions* was a valuable general journal, important in our period for the papers of Everard Home, Brodie, Bell and other zoologists and physiologists; it was beautifully printed in large quarto format, with very good engravings. In 1809 an abridged edition was published of the whole run of the journal from 1665 to 1800 in eighteen even larger volumes, with an extra volume of plates. Many papers are complete or nearly so, and brief biographies of contributors are often given; so that the run is a very useful compilation for the historian, giving a useful guide to what was seen (in 1800) as important in preceding researches. Other general journals, sometimes abstracting or reprinting papers from the *Philosophical Transactions* but also printing original papers, reports of the meetings of societies, translated papers, and reviews (both of books and of recent work in a field), began in Britain about 1800, and are useful to the historian although less splendid in printing and illustration — being on cheaper paper too, they have not kept as well and are often foxed or stained. The *Philosophical Magazine* and *Nicholson's Journal* were the two great rivals at the beginning of the century; having begun with a quarto format, Nicholson soon turned to an octavo size which remained general for the less expensive journals. In 1813 they were joined by *Annals of*

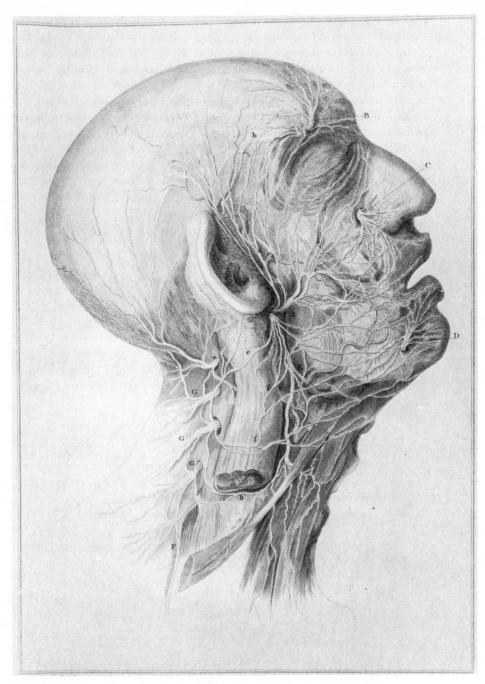

82　Dissection of a human head, from a paper by Bell in *Phil. Trans.*, *111* (1821)

Philosophy; this was edited by Thomas Thomson, a chemist, and had therefore a preponderance of chemical papers, but as time went on its emphasis became more geological and hence palaeontological. By 1830 all three had been amalgamated, the *Philosophical Magazine* having absorbed the others.

In other countries the pattern is not very different; the Academy of Sciences usually published a prestigious journal which came out rather slowly and contained papers from all the sciences. In America the only journal in this period was a general one, but was also private because there was no Academy or other central body; it was *Silliman's Journal*, which began in 1818 and still goes on, and it again contained much natural history and geology. But specialisation was a feature of the period, and as those who pursued the sciences came to see themselves as a distinct group, so the divisions between

83
Sea slugs, from *Magazine of Natural History*, 7 (1834) 584

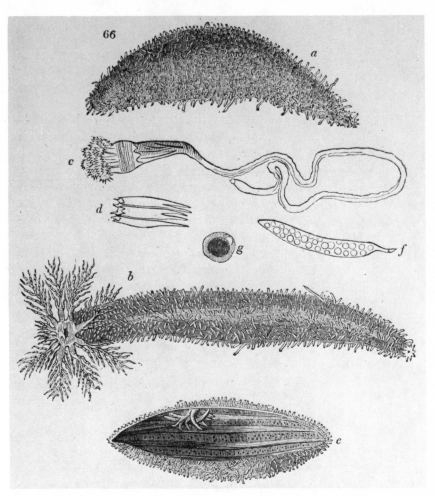

84
Catfish, from Shaw's *General
Zoology* (1800–1812)

them also became more obvious and those working in different disciplines
came to publish in different specialised journals. Thus Cuvier's researches
appeared first in the *Annales* of the Museum, as well as in publications of the
Institut and in the general *Journal de Physique*. In Britain the Linnean Society's
Transactions had begun to come out in 1791; the whole of natural history was
covered until 1875, when the journal separated into two parts, for zoology and
botany. In 1811 the Geological Society began its *Transactions*, a rather irregular
series, initially chiefly mineralogical but increasingly palaeontological by the
1820s; and in the same year the Wernerian Natural History Society in Edinburgh began to publish its memoirs. The great figure in the latter society was
Jameson, the Professor of Natural History, who was responsible for getting
Cuvier's *Theory of the Earth* translated into English in 1813. There was also the
Edinburgh Philosophical Journal under Brewster's editorship, publishing from
1819, and the *Transactions* of the Royal Society of Edinburgh in which Hutton,
Hall and other Plutonists published and which also included papers on
physiology and zoology. In 1828 Loudon began his *Magazine of Natural History*,
a private journal with emphasis on zoology; it is valuable as a guide to the
world of natural historians at this time, for papers came from both specialists
and amateurs, and controversy was sometimes fierce. It was illustrated with
wood engravings in the text rather than with copper-plates.

One of the editors of the abridged *Philosophical Transactions* was George
Shaw; he was responsible for the papers on natural history which he went
through carefully adding Linnean names. Shaw went up to Oxford in 1765,
and was ordained in 1774; but he gave up his career in the church because his
great interest was in zoology. He therefore went to Edinburgh and did a

medical training, and in 1787 set up in practice in London. He was one of the founders of the Linnean Society in 1788, and became a Vice-President; in 1791 he was appointed to the natural history section of the British Museum where he remained until his death. Shaw published a number of works, including a *Zoology of New Holland*, with plates by the great botanical artist James Sowerby; and a great compilation, *General Zoology*, of which eight volumes had appeared by 1812. Shaw died in 1813, and the remaining volumes, on birds, were written by J. F. Stephens. The octavo volumes have handsome engraved title-pages, and attractive engraved plates in the text; there are generic and specific descriptions in Latin and English, references to Linnaeus and authorities such as Bloch, and a short and readable account of each species.

Shaw was not the only person at this time to produce such a multi-volume and pleasantly-illustrated compendium. Edward Donovan was a keen entomologist who acquired Drury's collection, and went on to build up a large one of his own which he opened to the public in 1807 as the London Museum and Institute of Natural History. Donovan published various specialised works, including one useful to historians on how to collect and preserve natural history specimens; in the sphere of entomology, he published volumes on the insects of China, of New Holland, and of Asia — these were revised by Westwood in 1842. He also brought out handsomely illustrated compendia of British zoology: insects, birds, mammals, fishes, and shells, each set being composed of several volumes. On the whole, the insects and the fishes were the best depicted; later critics have found the attitudes of the mammals and birds stiff and unnatural, and their colouring overdone. Near the end of his life, Donovan published in 1833 a complaint against his publishers who, he claimed, owed him some £60,000 while he was in such penury that he could not even afford to take them to court; he also said that a complete set of his works would have cost about £100, which was a considerable sum but since so many volumes were involved is perhaps surprisingly small. Even if the £60,000 is an exaggeration, it does indicate that there was money to be made from what were relatively medium-priced publications.

The period from Linnaeus' definitive edition down to the death of Cuvier thus saw the appearance of numerous illustrated works on various levels of technicality and of sumptuousness. It marked the appearance of specialised journals and societies, and the growth of museums and zoos. It was a great age of scientific exploration, in which trained naturalists or doctors visited distant places and reported more or less accurately what they had seen. They also brought back specimens for those in the museums to classify. Classification went ahead rapidly, so that by the time of Cuvier's *Animal Kingdom* it had become much more certain and natural, though at the same time much more difficult, than it had been at the beginning of the period. In the following years, palaeontology continued to be of enormous importance as living and extinct species were classified, and then as theories of evolution and of inheritance changed the way in which scientists saw the animal kingdom.

Bibliography

Adams Jnr., G., *Essays on the Microscope*, 1787
Annals of Philosophy, 1 (1813)–16 (1820); new series, 1 (1821)–12(1826)
Anon, *A New System of Natural History*, 3 vols, Edinburgh, 1791–92
    A Natural History of Insects, Perth 1792
    Directions for Catching and Preparing Insects, undated. See also J. L. Knapp
Asiatick Researches, 1 (1788)–20 (1836);
Asiatic Society Bengal, *Journal*, 1 (1832)–
Proceedings, 1 (1865)–
Audebert, J. P., and Vieillot, P., *Les Oiseaux à Reflets Métalliques*, Paris 1802
Audubon, J. J. L., *The Birds of America*, 4 vols, 1827–38;
    Original Drawings, 2 vols, 1966;
    Ornithological Biography, 5 vols, Edinburgh 1831–39
Audubon, J. J. L., and Bachman, J., *Viviparous Quadrupeds of North America*, 5 vols, New York 1845–54
Bancroft, E., *The Natural History of Guiana*, 1769
Banks, J., *The Endeavour Journal, 1768–71*, J. C. Beaglehole (ed.), 2 vols, Sydney 1962;
    Joseph Banks in Newfoundland and Labrador, 1766, by A. M. Lysaght, 1971;
    The Banks Letters, W. R. Dawson (ed.), 1958
Barbut, J., *The Genera Insectorum of Linnaeus*, 1780;
    The Genera Vermium, 2 pts, 1783–88
Bartram, W., *Travels through North and South Carolina*, Philadelphia 1791;
    Botanical and Zoological Drawings, J. Ewan (ed.), Philadelphia 1968
Bell, C., *System of Dissections*, Edinburgh 1798;
    Essays on the Anatomy of Expression in Painting, 1806;
    The Great Operations of Surgery, 1821;
    The Natural System of the Nerves of the Human Body, 1824; supplement 1827;
    Animal Mechanics [1828];
    Nervous System of the Human Body, 1830;
    The Hand, 1833 (Bridgewater Treatise)
Bell, C. and Bell, J., *Anatomy of Human Body*, Edinburgh 1793–1804
Bennett, E. T., *The Tower Menagerie* 1829;
    The Gardens and Menagerie of the Zoological Society Delineated, 2 vols, 1830
Bewick, T., *History of British Birds*, 2 vols, Newcastle 1797–1804;
    General History of Quadrupeds, Newcastle 1790;
    Bibliography, S. Roscoe, 1973
Bingley, W., *Animal Biography*, 3 vols, 1802–03;
    British Quadrupeds, 1809
Blainville, H. M. D., *Manuel de Malacologie et Conchologie*, Paris 1825–27;
    Manuel sur les Belemnites, Paris 1827;
    Manuel d'Actinologie, 2 vols, Paris 1834;
    Osteographie, 8 vols, Paris 1839–64
Bloch, M. E., *Oeconomische Naturgeschichte der Fische Deutschlands*, 3 vols, Berlin, 1782–84;
    Naturgeschichte der Auslaendische Fische, 9 vols in 2, Berlin 1785–95
Blumenbach, J. F., *Abbildungen naturhistorischer Gegenstände*, 10 pts Göttingen 1797–1810
Bolton, J., *Harmonia Ruralis*, 2 vols, 1794–96

Bonaparte, C. L., *American Ornithology*, 4 vols, Philadelphia 1825–33;
  Iconographia della Fauna Italica, 3 vols, Rome 1832–41
Bowditch, T. E., *The Natural Classification of Mammalia*, Paris 1821;
  The Ornithology of Cuvier, 1821;
  Elements of Conchology, 1822;
  Excursions in Madeira and Porto Santo, 1825
Boys, W. and Walker, G., *Testacea Minuta Rariora*, 1784
Brisson, M. J., *Ornithologia*, 6 vols, Paris 1760
Brookes, R., *A New System of Natural History*, 6 vols, 1763
Brown, P., *New Illustrations of Zoology*, 1776
Brown, T., *Elements of Conchology*, 1816;
  Illustrations of Recent Conchology, 1827;
  Book of Butterflies, 2 vols, 1832;
  Zoologist's Text-book, 2 vols 1832;
  American Ornithology of Wilson and Bonaparte, 1835;
  Game Birds of North America, 1834;
  Fossil Conchology of Great Britain and Ireland, 1838–49;
  Land and Freshwater Conchology of Great Britain and Ireland, 1845 (*British Shells*)
Buckland, W., *Reliquiae Diluvianae*, 1823;
  Geology and Mineralogy, 2 vols, 1836 (Bridgewater Treatise)
Buffon, Comte de, (G. L. le Clerc), *Histoire Naturelle, Generale et Particuliere*, 44 volumes,
  Paris 1749; the enterprise was completed by C. J. M. Daubenton and B. G. E. de la
  V. Lacépède
Burrow, E. I., *Elements of Conchology*, 1815
Burtin, F. X., *Oryctographie de Bruxelles*, Brussels 1784
Camper, P., *Natuurkundige over den Orang Outang*, Amsterdam 1782;
  Oeuvres, 3 vols + atlas, Paris 1803
Carus, C. G., *Lehrbuch der Zootomie*, 1 vol. + atlas, 1818; English tr. 1827
Clairville, de J. P., *Entomologie Helvétique*, 2 vols, Zurich 1798–1806
Collins, D., *The English Colony in New South Wales*, 2 vols, 1798–1802
Cook, J., *A Voyage Towards the South Pole*, 2 vols, 1772;
  Journals, J. C. Beaglehole (ed.), 4 vols in 5, 1955–74;
  Forty Drawings of Fishes, P. J. P. Whitehead (ed.), 1968
Costa, E. M. da, *A Natural History of Fossils*, 1757;
  Elements of Conchology, 1776;
  Historia Naturalis Testaceorum Britanniae, 1778
Crabbe, G., *Natural History of the Vale of Belvoir*, 1795
Cramer, *Papillons Exotiques*, 4 vols, Amsterdam [1774]–1779–82
Curtis, J., *British Entomology*, 8 vols, 1824–39;
  Farm insects, 1883
Curtis, W., *The Brown-tail Moth*, 1782
Cuvier, G. L. C. F. D., *Recherches sur les Ossemens Fossiles*, 4 vols, Paris 1812;
  La Règne Animal, 4 vols, Paris 1816; new ('disciples') edn, 17 vols, 1836–49;
  The Animal Kingdom, E. Griffith *et al.* (tr.), 15 vols, 1827–34;
  Georges Cuvier, by W. Coleman, Cambridge, Mass. 1964
Cuvier, G. L. C. F. D. and Valenciennes, A., *Histoire Naturelle des Poissons*, 22 vols, Paris
  1828–49
  Fossils and Progress by P. Bowler, 1976
Daniell, S., *African Scenery and Animals*, 1804–05;
  The Scenery, Animals, and Native Inhabitants of Ceylon, 1808;
  The Native Tribes, Animals and Scenery of Southern Africa, 1820

Daniell, S. and Wood, W., *Zoography*, 3 vols, 1807
Desmarest, A. G., *Histoire Naturelle des Tangares*, Paris 1805
Donovan, E., *Natural History of British Insects*, 16 vols, 1792–1813;
   Instructions for Collecting, 1794;
   British Birds, 10 vols, 1794–1819;
   The Natural History of the Insects of China, 1798;
   The Natural History of the Insects of India, 1800–04;
   The Natural History of the Insects of New Holland, 1805;
   British Shells, 5 vols, 1799–1804;
   British Fishes, 5 vols, 1802–08;
   British Quadrupeds, 3 vols, 1820
Drury, D., *Illustrations of Natural History*, 3 vols, 1770–82;
   Exotic Entomology, J. O. Westwood (ed.), 3 vols, 1837
Edinburgh Philosophical Journal, 1(1819)–14(1826); *Ed. New Phil. J.*, 1(1826)–57(1854),
   new series 1(1855)–19(1864)
Ellis, J., *An Essay towards a Natural History of the Corallines*, 1755;
   The Natural History of Zoophytes, D. Solander (ed.), 1786;
   Starfish, Jellyfish and the Order of Life by M. P. Winsor, New Haven 1976
Encyclopedia Britannica, 3 vols, Edinburgh 1771; by the 9th edn, 24 vols, 1875, the
   illustrations have moved onto the pages of text.
   Encyclopedias, a bibliographical guide, by R. L. E. Collison, New York 1964;
   Anglo-American General Encyclopedias, by S. P. Walsh, New York 1968
Encyclopedia Metropolitana, 29 vols, 1817–45
Encyclopédie, 35 vols, Paris 1751–80
Encyclopédie Méthodique, 201 vols, Paris 1782–1832
Fabricius, J. C. F. and Panzer, G. W., *Faunae Insectorum Germanicae*, Nuremberg and
   Regensburg 1792–1844
Fabricius, O. F., *Fauna Groen Landika*, Leipzig 1780
Fenn, E., *Short History of Insects*, Norwich 1797
Fitzgerald, F., *Surveys of Nature*, 2 vols, [c 1789]
Fleming, J., *The Philosophy of Zoology*, Edinburgh 1822
Forster, J. G. A., *Vögel der Südsee, 1772–5*, Leipzig 1971;
   A Voyage Round the World, 2 vols, 1772–75;
   A Journey from Bengal to England, 2 vols, 1798
Forster, J. R., *The Animals of North America*, 1771;
   Observations Made During a Voyage Round the World, 1778;
   Indische Zoologie (based on Pennant), Halle 1781
Forster, T. I. M., *Observations on Swallows*, 1808; 6th edn, 1817
Franklin, J., *Narrative of a Journey to the Shores of the Polar Sea*, 1823;
   A Second Journey, 1828
Fuessly, J., *Histoire des Insectes*, Winterthur 1794
Gall, F. J. and Spurzheim, J. G., *Anatomie et physiologie du Système Nervaux*, 4 vols + atlas,
   Paris 1810–19
Geoffroy Saint Hilaire, E., *Philosophie Anatomique*, Paris 1818–22;
   Etudes Progressives d'un Naturaliste, Paris 1835
Gilpin, W., *Forest Scenery*, 2 vols, 1791
Girton, D., *A Treatise on Domestic Pigeons*, 1765
Gmelin, C. C., *Gemeinnützige Systematische Naturgeschichte der Vögel*, Mannheim 1809
Goldsmith, O., *The Earth and Animated Nature*, 8 vols, 1774
Gronovius, L. T., *Museum Ichthyologicum*, 2 vols, Leyden 1754
Hamilton, F. (Buchanan), *An Account of the Fishes Found in the River Ganges*, 1822;

A Journey from Madras, 1807

Harris, M., *The Aurelian*, 1758–66;
   English Insects, 1776–80

Haworth, A. H., *Lepidoptera Britannica*, 1803–12

Hayes, M., *Natural History of British Birds*, 1775;
   Portraits of Rare and Curious Birds, 1794

Holt, J., *The Agriculture of Lancaster*, 1795

Home, E., *Lectures on Comparative Anatomy*, 4 vols, 1814–23; supplement, 2 vols, 1828

Horsfield, T., *Zoological Researches in Java*, 1821–24

Huber, F., *Nouvelles Observations sur les Abeilles*, Paris 1792

Huber, J. P., *Recherches sur les Moeurs des Fourmis Indigènes*, Paris 1810

Humboldt, A. von., *Voyage aux Régions Equinoxiales du Nouveau Continent*, 30 vols, Paris 1805–30 (vols 23 and 24 are on zoology)

Hunter, J., *Works*, J. F. Palmer (ed.), 4 vols + atlas, 1835–37;
   Observations on Certain Parts of the Animal Economy, R. Owen (ed.), 1837;
   Essays and Observations, R. Owen (ed.), 2 vols, 1861

Ingpen, A., *Instructions for Collecting, Rearing and Preserving Insects*, 1827

Jesse, E., *Gleanings in Natural History*, 3 pts, 1832–5

Kalm, P., *Travels into North America*, J. R. Forster (tr.), 3 vols, Warrington 1770–71

Kirby, W., *The Creation of Animals*, 2 vols, 1835 (Bridgewater Treatise)

Kirby, W., and Spence, W., *Introduction to Entomology*, 4 vols, 1815–26;
   see also J. Richardson, *Fauna Boreali-Americana*

[Knapp], J. L., *Journal of a Naturalist*, 1829

Labillardiere, J. J., *Voyage à la recherche de La Perouse*, 2 vols + atlas, Paris 1800

Lacépède, B. G. E. de la V., *Histoire Naturelle*, M. A. G. Desmarest (ed.), 2 vols, Paris 1856; see also under Buffon

Lacépède, B. G. E. de la V., and Cuvier, G., *Menagerie du Museum d'Histoire Naturelle*, Paris 1801

Lamarck, J. B., *Mémoire sur les Fossiles*, Paris 1802–06

La Perouse, J. F. G., *Voyage Autour la Monde*, 4 vols, Paris 1797

Latham, J., *A General Synopsis of Birds*, 3 vols, 1781–83; index, 1790; supplements 1787 and 1801;
   General History of Birds, 10 vols, Winchester 1821–28

Lavater, J. C., *Physiognomische Fragmente*, 4 vols, Leipzig 1778

Leach, W. E., *Malacostrata Podophthalmata Britanniae*, 1815–75;
   Molluscorum Britanniae Synopsis, J. E. Gray (ed.), 1852

Lettsom, J., *The Naturalist's Companion*, 1772

Levaillant, F., *Histoire Naturelle des Perroquets*, 2 vols, Paris 1801–05;
   Histoire Naturelle des Oiseaux d'Afrique, 6 vols, Paris 1805–08;
   Histoire Naturelle des Oiseaux de Paradis, des Promerops, 3 vols, 1807;
   supplement to the *Perroquets*, by A. B. Saint-Hilaire, Paris 1837–38

Lewin, J. W., *Lepidopterous insects of New South Wales*, 1805;
   Birds of New Holland, 1808

Lewin, W., *The Birds of Great Britain*, 7 vols, 1789–94;
   Insects of Great Britain, 1795; another issue has title *Papilios* . . .

Lichtenstein, M. H. K., *Travels in Southern Africa*, A. Plumptre (tr.), 2 vols, 1812–15

Linnean Society, *Transactions*, 1 (1791)–30 (1875); thereafter zoology and botany came out in separate series;
   History of the Linnean Society by A. T. Gage, 1938

Lord, T., *Entire New System of Ornithology*, 1791

Lyonet, P., *Traité Anatomique de la Chenille*, The Hague 1760;

Recherches sur l'Anatomie . . ., Paris 1832

Macleay, W. S., *Annulosa Javanica*, 1815

Magazine of Natural History, 1 (1828)–9 (1836); second series, 1 (1837)–4 (1840); then joined with *Annals of Natural History*

Manchester Literary and Philosophical Society, *Memoirs*, 1 (1785)–

Manetti, X., *Ornithologia*, Florence 1767–76

Mantell, G., *The Fossils of the South Downs*, 1822;
  Wonders of Geology, 2 vols, 1838;
  Medals of Creation, 1844;
  Atlas of Fossil Remains, 1850, from Parkinson
  Petrifications and their Teachings, 1851;

Marey, E. J., *La Machine Animale*, Paris 1873, English tr. 1874;
  Le Mouvement, Paris 1894, English tr. 1895

Marsden, W., *History of Sumatra*, 1783; 3rd edn, 1811

Martyn, T., *The Universal Conchologist*, 4 vols, 1784–92;
  The English Entomologist, 1792;
  Aranei, 1793;
  Psyche, 1797

Martyn, W., *New Dictionary of Natural History*, 2 vols, 1785

Miller, J. F., *Various Subjects of Natural History*, 1776–94; new edn, G. Shaw (ed.), called *Cimelia physica*, 1796

Miller, J. S., *A Natural History of the Crinoidea*, Bristol 1821

Montagu, G., *Ornithological Dictionary*, 2 vols, 1802; later edns 1831 and 1866;
  Testacea Britannica, 2 pts, 1803; supplement 1808

Müller, O. F., *Zoologica Danica*, 2 vols + atlas, Leipzig 1779–84

Museum d'Histoire Naturelle, Paris, *Annales*, 1 (1802)–21 (1827);
  Nouvelles Annales, 1 (1832)–4 (1835);
  Mémoires, 1 (1815)–20 (1832);
  Archives, 1 (1839)–10 (1861);
  Nouvelles Archives, 1 (1865)–10 (1874), and then new series each decade

Mutis, J., *Flora de La Real Expedition (1760–1817)*, S. Rivas-Goday and E. Perez-Arbelaez (eds.), Madrid 1954–

Naumann, J. A., *Naturgeschichte der Land und Wasservögel*, 4 vols, Koethen 1795–1803; et al., *Naturgeschichte der Vögel Deutschlands*, 12 vols, Leipzig 1820–44, supplement 2 vols, 1860

Nicholson's (W.) *Journal of Natural Philosophy*, 1 (1797)–5 (1802), new series, 1 (1802)–36 (1813)

Nicolas, P. F., *Méthode de Préparer et Conserver les Animaux de Toutes les Classes*, Paris 1801

Nozeman, C., *Nederlandsche Vogelen*, Amsterdam 1770–1829

Osbaldiston, W., *The British Sportsman*, 1792

Paley, W., *Natural Theology*, J. Paxton (ill.), 2 vols, Oxford 1826; an illustrated version of this famous book which appeared in 1802

Pallas, P. S., *Spicelegia Zoologica*, 2 vols, Berlin 1767–80;
  Reise durch Verschiedene Provinzen des Russischen Reichs, 3 vols, St Petersburg 1771–76;
  Novae Species Quadrupedum, Erlangen 1778–79;
  Icones Insectorum, Erlangen 1781–98;
  Reise in die Südlichen Statthalterschaften des Russischen Reichs, 2 vols, Leipzig 1799–1801, English tr. 1802–3;
  Zoographia Russo-Asiatica, 3 vols, St Petersburg 1811–42;
  U. Urness (ed.), *A Naturalist in Russia*, Minneapolis 1967

Parkinson, J., *Organic Remains of a Former World*, 3 vols, 1804–11

Pennant, T., *British Zoology*, 4 vols, 1768–70; earlier version, by T. P., 2 vols, 1766;
  Indian Zoology, 1769;
  Synopsis of Quadrupeds, 1771, later edition called *History . . .*, 2 vols, 1781;
  Arctic Zoology, 2 vols, 1784–85, supplement 1787
Peron, F., *Voyage de Decouvertes aux Terres Australes*, 2 vols + atlas, Paris 1807–16;
  see N. Baudin, *Journal*, C. Cornell (tr.), Adelaide 1974
Phillip, A., *The Voyage of Governor Phillip to Botany Bay*, 1789
Philosophical Magazine, 1 (1798)–
Raffles, T. S., *History of Java*, 2 vols, 1817;
  Natural History in the India Office Library by M. Archer, 1962;
  Raffles Drawings, 1977
Rees, A., *The Cyclopedia*, 39 vols, 1819–20
Reeves, J., *Chinese Natural History Drawings*, P. J. P. Whitehead and P. I. Edwards (eds.),
  1974
Richardson, J., (and Swainson, W., Kirby, W., and Sowerby, J. de C.), *Fauna Boreali-
  Americana*, 3 vols, 1829–37;
  Icones Piscium, 1843
Richardson, J., and Gray, J. E., *Zoology of the Voyage of HMS Erebus & Terror*, 2 vols,
  1844–75
Riley, G., *Beauties of the Creation*, 2 vols, 1790; 2nd edn, 5 vols, 1793
Risso, A., *Ichthyologie de Nice*, Paris 1810
Roxburgh, W., *Icones Roxburghianae*, Calcutta 1964–
Royal Institution, *Quarterly Journal of Science and the Arts*, 1 (1816)–20 (1826), new series,
  1 (1827)–7 (1830);
  Proceedings, 1 (1851–4)–
Royal Society of Edinburgh, *Transactions*, 1 (1788)–
Rüppell, W. P. E. S., *Atlas zu der Reise im Nord Afrika*, Frankfurt 1826–8;
  Neue Wirbelthiere, Frankfurt 1835–40, supplement 1845
  Vögel Nord-Ost-Afrikas, Frankfurt 1845
Russell, P., *An Account of Indian Serpents*, 2 vols, 1796–1801;
  Two Hundred Fishes Collected at Vizagapatam, 2 vols, 1803
Scharf, G., *Six Views of the Zoological Gardens, Regent's Park*, 1835
Schroeter, J. S., *Die Geschichte der Flussconchylien*, Halle 1779;
  Musei Gottwaldiani Testaceorum, Nuremberg, 1782;
  Einleitung in die concylienkenntniss, 3 vols, Halle 1783–6
Scoresby, W., *An Account of the Arctic Regions*, 2 vols, Edinburgh 1820
Selby, P. J., *Illustrations of British Ornithology*, 1821–34
Shaw, G., *Speculum Linneanum*, 1790;
  General Zoology, 14 vols, 1800–26;
  Zoological Lectures, 2 vols, 1809
Shaw, G., and Nodder, F. P., *The Naturalist's Miscellany*, 2 vols, 1799–1813
Sibly, E., *An Universal System of Natural History*, 14 vols, 1794–1807
B. Silliman's *American Journal of Science and Arts*, 1 (1818)–
Smith, J. E., *The Rarer Lepidopterous Insects of Georgia*, 2 vols, 1797
Smith, R., *Universal Directory for Taking Alive and Destroying Vermin*, 1768
Smith, W., *Strata Identified by Organised Fossils*, 1816;
  Stratigraphical System of Organised Fossils, 1817
Sonnerat, P., *Voyage à la Nouvelle Guinée*, Paris 1776;
  Voyages aux Indes Orientales, Paris 1782
Sowerby, J., *The British Miscellany*, 2 vols, 1804–07;
  The Mineral Conchology of Great Britain, 7 vols, 1812–46;

   The Genera of Recent and Fossil Shells, 2 vols, 1820–34

Spallanzani, L., *Opuscoli di Fisica Animale*, Modena 1776; English tr. 1784, new edn 1789
   Dissertazioni, Modena 1780; English tr. 1799, new edn 1803

Sparrman, A., *Resa till Goda Hops-Udden*, Stockholm 1783; English tr. 1786;
   Museum Carlsonianum, 4 vols, Holmiae 1786–89

Spix, J. B., *Simiarum et Vespertilionum Brasiliensium*, 1823;
   Serpentum Brasiliensium, 1824;
   Testudinem et Ranarum, 1824;
   Avium, 1825;
   Lacertarum, 1825;
   Testacea fluviatilia, 1827;
   Animalium articulatum, Monachii 1830–34

Spix, J. B., and Agassiz, L., *Selecta Genera et Species Piscium Brasiliam*, Leipzig 1829–30

Spix, J. B., and Martius, C. F. P., *Reise in Brasilien*, 3 vols + atlas, Munich 1823–31

Stead, J., *Description and Natural History of English Song Birds*, 1797

Stedman, J. G., *A Five Year's Expedition Against the Revolted Negroes in Surinam*, 2 vols, 1796;
   Journal, S. Thompson (ed.), 1962

Stephens, J. F., *Illustrations of British Entomology*, 12 vols, 1827–46;
   Bibliotheca Stephensoniana, 1853, including memoir

Stubbs, G., *The Anatomy of the Horse*, 1766;
   A Comparative Anatomical Exposition of the Human Body, the Tiger, and the Common Fowl, 1803–06

Susemihl, J. C., *Abbildungen aus dem Thierreiche*, Darmstadt 1821–26;
   Abbildungen der Vögel Europas, Stuttgart 1839–51

Thompson, J. V., *Zoological Researches and Illustrations*, Cork 1828–34

Vieillot, J. P., *Histoire Naturelle des Plus Beaux Oiseaux Chanteur de la Zone Torride*, Paris 1805–;
   Histoire Naturelle des Oiseaux de l'Amerique Septentrionale, 2 vols, Paris 1807;
   Vieillot, J. P. (ed.), *Faune Française*, 8 vols, 4 vols + atlas, Paris 1820–30

Vieillot, J. P., and Oudart, P. L., *La Galerie des Oiseaux*, 2 vols, Paris 1820–26;
   Ornithologie Française, Paris, 1823–30 and 1907

Wakefield, P., *Introduction to Entomology*, 1815

Walton, W., *The Peruvian Sheep*, 1818;
   The Alpaca, 1844

Waterton, C., *Wanderings in South America*, 1825;
   Essays on Natural History, 1838

Wernerian Society, Edinburgh, *Memoirs*, 1(1811)–8(1839)

White, G., *The Natural History and Antiquities of Selborne*, 1789;
   Bibliography, by E. A. Martin, new edn, 1970

Wildman, T., *A Treatise on the Management of Bees*, 1768

Wilkes, B, *Twelve New Designs of English Butterflies*, 1742;
   English Moths and Butterflies, 1749; 2nd edn, called *One hundred and twenty Copper-plates . . .*, 1773

Wilson, A., *American Ornithology*, 9 vols Philadelphia 1808–14; another edn, 4 vols, Edinburgh 1831

Zoological Journal, 1(1825)–4(1835)

Zoological Miscellany, 1(1814)–3(1817); revived, 1(1831)–6(1844)

5

The Modern Period

By the 1830s the separation of the various sciences was well under way, and careers in the sciences were opening up. Whereas earlier a man of science required private means or a profession, needed to be a great opportunist or find a patron — hence the differences in the careers of various zoologists — by the middle of the nineteenth century entry into the ranks of zoologists was along more beaten tracks, and there were beginning to be opportunities in museums, in colleges and hospitals, and as collectors overseas, for those who expected to live by their science. The collection and depiction of animals was beginning to give way to the study of their distribution, their anatomy and physiology, and their place in the taxonomic scheme.

Zoological works tended during the century — just like books and journals in other sciences — to become more technical. Books which earlier would have been directed both at the learned world and at a general readership become rarer, and we find learned works with clear but not always especially beautiful illustrations, popular works with illustrations and text of varying degrees of beauty and accuracy, and then luxurious 'coffee table' books of great size and splendour, beyond the means of men of science unless they were magnates and patrons of science like Lord Derby. Anatomy and physiology had already become too technical for the general reader, and while Richard Owen was disappointed at the small sales of his various monographs he should not have been surprised. It is indeed in some ways more surprising how stiff a diet the Victorian general reader could take; the gulf between the technical and the popular book or paper was opening, but it had not yet — and has not yet — become such that none can pass from one side to the other. Men such as Hugh

Miller, who described the fishes of the Old Red Sandstone, moved from the position of a populariser to that of a scientist; while eminent researchers became their own popularisers, in lectures or in books, as T. H. Huxley did.

While much had been added to geography since Cook's time, there were still regions unvisited by scientific men, and regional studies were still of fundamental importance through most of the nineteenth century. Africa was a completely unknown quantity, and we therefore find men like Owen and Murchison encouraging Livingstone and others in their travels just as Banks had supported Mungo Park. The existence of the Mountains of the Moon, and of the great peaks of East Africa, and the courses of the Niger, the Congo, and the Nile were all problematic, and could only be settled by expeditions. The expeditions could also contribute to the knowledge of flora and fauna; but in such endeavours, particularly to West Africa, fever took its toll — on Tuckey's expedition to the Zaïre in 1816 all the naturalists except the botanic gardener died, and should presumably be described as martyrs to science.

The western parts of North America were rather better known, for Lewis and Clark had crossed further south than Mackenzie, and Spanish soldiers and missionaries were coming up through the south-west to the California missions, while further to the north the fur traders of Astoria and of the Hudson's Bay Company were covering vast distances. What was lacking was exact knowledge; and accurate descriptions of the fauna, the flora, and the geology were made particularly from the mid-century on. Audubon, with Bachman, brought out in 1845–6 in two vast volumes his *Viviparous Quadrupeds of North America*, with three volumes of text; the pictures are splendid but a slight disappointment after the *Birds*, being often rather stiff.

Really serious science is to be found in the various government reports on the American West, and indeed also in state surveys in the settled parts of the country. The explorations to find a route for the transcontinental or Pacific Railroad which were undertaken by the Federal Government in the 1850s, with surveys done by the Corps of Topographical Engineers of the Army, were very handsomely published indeed; and the illustrations of plants, animals and fossils as well as of romantic little camps in wild territory make these Reports some of the most attractive natural history publications of the nineteenth century. Further to the north, expeditions from Britain in search of a North-West passage yielded much data, and the material was organised into *Fauna Boreali-Americana* by Richardson, the doctor on Sir John Franklin's expeditions down the Coppermine and Mackenzie rivers. Richardson wrote up the fishes, Kirby the insects, and Swainson the birds. Money was provided by the government for the cost of the engravings; and the volumes, which superseded Pennant's *Arctic Zoology*, were very handsome as well as having a text of considerable importance. Swainson's volume on birds is beautifully illustrated — he was one of the greatest depictors of birds ever — but the text is curious, because he was a convert to the so-called quinary system of classification, in which species were grouped in fivefold divisions which formed circles, so that in any natural group one did not find linear progression but rather that extremes met. This theoretical commitment reduced the usefulness and working life of what had been meant to be a descriptive volume.

The interior of Australia was as unknown as that of Africa, but as the century wore on it gradually became clear that it did not contain the hoped-for inland sea. Fossils were found there, and were sent to Owen who found that they were of marsupials; and the birds and mammals of the continent were written up by John Gould in a series of enormous volumes which make him the Audubon of Australia. Gould's works were more serious science than Audubon's; the bird illustrations are hand coloured lithographs, those based on drawings by Elizabeth Gould being generally felt to be the best, although some of Richter's are excellent. Because Elizabeth Gould died soon after the family returned from Australia, the bulk of the pictures were done by Richter; and in depicting a whole family of birds in plate after plate — and Gould was a splitter, separately illustrating what would now be called sub-species — it is difficult not to fall into a formula. Some of the plates show the bird wounded, reminding us of what a sanguinary process natural-history collecting was; others are drawn from a single specimen, sometimes even just a skin of doubtful provenance sent to Gould — the plates from these were bound to be less satisfactory than those of birds Gould or one of his team of collectors had actually observed in the field. Like Audubon's (but less so) Gould's mammals are a little disappointing, though not to be despised; their shapes and colours

85
A nondescript from Australia; wombat, from Collins' *New South Wales* (1798–1802)

158

86   A forest wallaby, from Gould's *Mammals of Australia* (1845–60)

87   Hawks, by Wolf, from Siebold's *Fauna Japonica* (1833–50)

are less attractive, and to draw them well requires even more knowledge of anatomy than it does to create attractive pictures of birds.

From the Far East came the *Illustrations of Indian Zoology* of Gray (of the British Museum) and General Hardwicke, who had collected pictures by native artists of the fauna of India. These were copied onto stone by Waterhouse Hawkins, along with some pictures done for Reeves in China, and made a superb picture-book; for there is no text, the animals being simply named by Gray, with sometimes a caption of dubious value — the Reeves pheasant, for example, which is shown reduced and reversed from one of Reeves' pictures, is described as drawn under his supervision from life when in fact it seems that the drawing, still in the British Museum (Natural History), was a stock one purchased by Reeves.

A more important work on the oriental region was the *Fauna Japonica* of Siebold, which was the first work to go beyond Kaempfer's *History of Japan* of 1727. Like Kaempfer, Siebold had visited the country in 1823 as a doctor with the Dutch Ship that went annually to Nagasaki; he had remained some seven years in Japan, confined to a little island in Nagasaki harbour for most of the time except when once a year the Dutchmen went to pay their respects to the Shogun in Tokyo. With the assistance of Japanese interpreters, he built up a considerably stock of specimens, and collected much information. On his return, the Dutch East India Company supported the publication of his results; the birds were described by Temminck, while other authorities helped Siebold with descriptions of other groups. Some of the fish were drawn by Keiga Kawahara, the other illustrations being by prominent European illustrators; and between 1833 and 1850 the book came out in five splendid volumes. This was the last western work on Japan that had to be written in this curiously hole-and-corner way, for in July 1853 Commodore Perry's black ships entered Tokyo Bay; and indeed on that expedition zoological information was collected, and drawings made.

Asia was not *terra incognita* like Africa or Australia; once again the question was exactly where geographical features were, rather than whether they existed. In India, J. F. Royle published between 1833 and 1840 his *Illustrations of the Botany and other Branches of the Natural History of the Himalyan Mountains*; he was a surgeon and botanist, but the book contains descriptions of the entomology and mammalology of the area too, and is well illustrated. The classic work on the *Birds of India* was Jerdon's — he being a surgeon in the Madras service — with plates, 1847, fuller but unillustrated, 1862–4; Baker's work on *Indian Ducks* (1908) is a very attractive study indeed, with splendid plates by Grönvold, Lodge, and Keulemans, allowing for a comparison of styles and depicting some birds familiar to European readers such as the mallard, and others that are exotic. Horsfield and Vigors described birds, mammals, and insects in the East India Company's museum; and in 1861 J. E. Tennent's *Sketches of the Natural History of Ceylon* was published. It is illustrated with wood

88
Diagram of a bird, from
Jerdon's *Birds of India* (1877
edn)

engravings, and is particularly valuable for its material on elephants. Other regional studies such as Marsden's *History of Sumatra* (1783, with an enlarged third edition in 1811) and Raffles' *History of Java* (1817) are valuable for their natural history. In a lighter vein, there is E. H. A. [Aitken], *Tribes on my Frontier*, 1883.

The standard work on the birds of New Zealand was by Buller, illustrated by Keulemans; it is curious that after the first edition (1873) the stones were wiped so that no more plates could be printed from them, and so the second edition (1887) had quite new and different plates by the same artist, one of the best and most versatile illustrators of the time. The leading early work on the zoology of South Africa was Smith's *Illustrations*, of 1838–49. In South America, there were many who trod in Humboldt's footsteps, the most famous being Charles Darwin, whose volumes on the zoology and geology of the voyage of the *Beagle* in addition to his famous account of the expedition, were chiefly concerned with South American specimens. Robert Schomburgk described some of the fauna of Central America, and Azara the quadrupeds of Paraguay; but the most splendid illustrated works from this region were

162

probably those of Descourtilz. In 1835 his *Oiseaux brillans et remarquable du Brésil* appeared, but in such a small edition (single figures) that it hardly counts as being published at all! The text was handwritten and was not printed until 1960, when it was published with a handsome facsimile of the lithographed plates, which are some of the most decorative and lifelike ever made. The birds are shown on plants they frequent, or with their usual prey.

Among the birds shown by Descourtilz are humming-birds, on which John Gould did a monograph (1849–1861) illustrated with splendid plates by Richter; while in Mexico, Montes de Oca in the 1870s did some attractive paintings of humming-birds and orchids, which make a pleasing combination — these remained unpublished until 1963. On the whole Descourtilz's illustrations remained barely accessible, although in 1854 — shortly before his death by poison when experimenting with a medicine for birds — his *Ornithologie Brésilienne* was published in Rio de Janeiro, with plates (different from those in the *Oiseaux brillans*) printed in London.

There were also regional studies made in less exotic places, of which Gould's *Birds of Great Britain* (1867–73) can be mentioned because one of the artists involved in it was Josef Wolf, who to contemporaries (and to critics since) seemed to be perhaps the finest of all illustrators of natural history. Wolf had a

89
Plate by Grönvold from Baker's *Indian Ducks* (1908)

163

90
The pursuit of pleasure.
Chameleon and butterfly,
from E. H. A. [Aitken],
Tribes on my Frontier (1909
edn)

firm grasp of anatomy, and had carefully and lovingly observed wild animals, so that his pictures are both accurate and valuable from the zoological point of view, and also very lifelike. Unlike Baker, whose primary interest in ducks was as game, Wolf was opposed to field sports.

Regional studies are as a rule theory-free, though some theory may find its way into them as it did into Swainson's work on Arctic birds. Such a study may however lead to a new theory, as did Darwin's study of the fauna of South America and of the Galapagos Islands; and as the studies of distribution of animals and plants did for Alfred Russel Wallace, who hit upon the idea of evolution by natural selection before Darwin had published his views. Wallace's descriptions of his journeys as a collector of specimens on the Amazon and in the Malay archipelago are very famous, and led him to his idea of different faunas being confined to different zones with sometimes — as between Bali and Lombok — a surprisingly sharp frontier between them. Among Wallace's books is *Island Life* (1880), for to the evolutionist the isolated communties of creatures on islands are of much interest. Island life-forms had been earlier discussed in a regional study which seems on the surface extremely dry and specialised: T. V. Wollaston's *Insecta Maderiensa* (1854). This account of the insects of Madeira by a member of an extremely distinguished scientific family is interesting because the author had to investigate the

164

distribution as well as the classification of insects, and had to decide which of those that seemed confined to Madeira were species, and which were varieties. He followed up this study with an essay *On the variation of species* (1856), used by Darwin as a source when writing the *Origin of Species* (1859).

The notorious quinary system had been proposed by MacLeay in cataloguing insects collected by Horsfield in Java, and was described by him in *Annulosa*

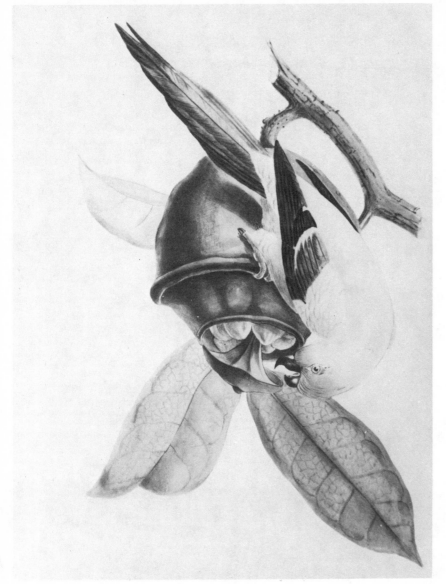

91
Parrot, from Descourtilz's
Oiseaux brillans du Brésil
(1835)

Clap Net.

Sweeping Net.

Fly Extended.

Bonnet Net.

Insect with Single Braces.

Insect with Double Braces.

Emperor Net.

Store Box.

Setting Case.

Pocket Box.

Breeding Case.

Sugar Tin.

Chloroform Bottle.

Box for Pill Boxes.

Digger.

Thread Spool.

Relaxing Jar.

Insect on Tarred Wood.

92   Equipment for an entomological collector, from Morris' *British Butterflies* (1895 edn)

Javanica; or an attempt to illustrate the natural affinities and analogies of the insects . . .
(1815). Another attempt to divert taxonomists from the lines laid down by
Cuvier — following Aristotle — was John Fleming's *Philosophy of Zoology*
(1822), in which he proposed a dichotomous system in place of Cuvier's use of
multiple criteria in determining natural groups. Fleming also wrote a *History of
British Animals* (1828) which in its numbers of species and genera was an
advance on previous catalogues; but despite this his system of classification
did not catch on. Those who came after Cuvier generally followed his
approach, though they frequently differed over what were generic or specific
differences, and which forms were varieties and which were species; 'splitters'
like Gould often counted as different species what would now be regarded as
sub-species having different geographical ranges, or as differently-pigmented
forms of one species. Taxonomists differed over the weighting to be assigned to
various characters, while agreeing that several characters should be taken into
account: few in the nineteenth century seem to have followed Adanson's
notion that there should be no weighting, making for a taxonomy without
preconceptions. However even with an open class of characters, when one has
numbered all that one can think of there may still be many that one ought to
have thought of.

One of the great problems facing taxonomists was the classification of fossil
species; and the close alliance between geologists and zoologists through
palaeontology, which had begun with the work of Cuvier and of Smith, was a
feature of the later nineteenth century too. As a rule, in scientific works the
bones were simply figured, but there were sometimes artistic reconstructions
of what the animal might have looked like. One of the more dramatic of these is
the picture by John Martin, famous for his enormous apocalyptic canvases, of
The Country of the Iguanadon, which forms the frontispiece of Mantell's
Wonders of Geology (1838, with many later editions). Highlighted in the rather
murky engraving are various fighting dragons (iguanadons, misunderstood so
that their thumbs appear as horns and their posture is wrong) while others in
the background are aggressively displaying, and in the foreground are some
tortoises and ammonites, with a pterodactyl. The text incorporated sober
wood-engravings of teeth and skeletons, as befitted a work of science, even if
popular science, by one of the first men to identify a dinosaur.

Buckland's *Reliquiae Diluvianae* (1823) had brought him fame, but contemporary geologists were soon weaned away by Scrope and Lyell towards the
belief that geological processes operated over vast periods of time, and had
been the same in the past as in the present. Some, like Murchison, continued to
hold that there had been convulsions when the processes had operated more
violently; but too much reliance upon the Flood became unfashionable, and
Buckland's book was irreverently called 'Idola Specus'. He was chosen to
write the Bridgewater Treatise (1836) showing the goodness of God from the
facts of geology, and to the relief of his fellows he no longer insisted upon the

167

Flood. Palaeontology is very prominent, and indeed dominant; there is a splendid coloured fold-out plate over a metre long, showing the various strata with their characteristic populations of plants and animals as well as some active volcanoes. Other handsome plates show different kinds of fossils, including coprolites in which Buckland and his contemporaries took a great interest believing them to be the fossilised faeces of extinct creatures, giving therefore valuable evidence about the states of their insides. Less recondite fossils depicted were the footprints of various reptiles; Buckland indeed enlivened a scientific meeting by hopping about to demonstrate how such prints might have been made. His abandonment of the Flood as the chief agent of geological change did not bring him into any ecclesiastical disfavour, for in 1845 he was made Dean of Westminster.

Buckland's fold-out plate included the Silurian system, which consisted of secondary rocks called grauwacke, which had been supposed to contain very few fossils, for in the early days of stratigraphy it was the tertiary rocks that had been most easy to put in order from their fossils. The Silurian system was worked out in the 1830s by Murchison, a soldier and fox-hunting man who had been drawn into science by Sir Humphry Davy and propelled further in by his wife. Murchison's *Silurian System* of 1839 was a handsome quarto which as well as geological sections conained pictures of characteristic fossils of the Silurian rocks. With Sedgewick, who had been Darwin's mentor in geology, Murchison founded the Devonian system also; and then on an expedition to the Ural mountains he founded the Permian system. He had worked out the Silurian rocks in South Wales, while Sedgewick had been unravelling the sequence of rocks in the north of that province, calling them Cambrian. Murchison's rate of publication was higher, and Sedgewick found some of his Cambrian fossils taken over by Murchison and described as Lower Silurian; this led to one of the most celebrated rows and estrangements in Victorian science. Both protagonists were sufficiently cataclysmic in their view of the Earth's history to see the various epochs as more than convenient and conventional divisions; and both felt that the other was trying to take over their rocks and fossils.

The ability to walk miles over rough country, to spot changes in the structure of the rocks, and to find fossils, is not necessarily or even probably coexistent with the ability to identify those fossils accurately. The field geologist of the nineteenth century developed a feel for the sort of fossils that characterised a certain system of rocks; but the fine discriminations demanded the resources of the museum, and the training of the comparative anatomist. Men like Murchison attracted the limelight, but their work would not have been possible without the careful comparisons of fossils made by such men as Lonsdale, who looked after the Geological Society's collections, of J. de C. and G. B. Sowerby — the conchologist members of the famous family — John Phillips, Owen, and in France men like de Verneuil. Of these, only the Sowerbys and Owen attracted any great attention in the outside world; for in

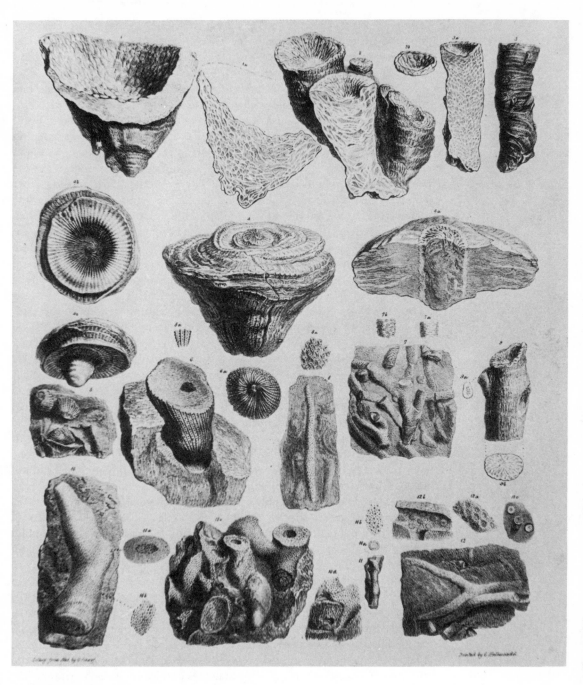

93   Fossil corals, from Murchison's *Silurian System* (1839)

science as elsewhere there were some who grasped the skirts of happy chance and went on to fame and fortune, while others whose merits were equal or superior remained in relative obscurity — but enjoyed perhaps greater happiness than those who caught the public eye.

Murchison's visits to Russia made him an admirer of the Tsar, whom he met and who later presented him with a vase and a snuff box of great splendour that can now be seen in South Kensington at the Geological Museum; but it also helped him to get straight some of the sequences of rocks in Scotland and in Devonshire. Strata 'missing' in one part of the world may well be found elsewhere; and travel abroad was as important for the geologist as for the zoologist; the gaps in the geological record were gradually filled in and further gaps revealed. In France there had been a school of mines since the late eighteenth century; Werner at the mining academy at Freiberg from 1775 had attracted students from all over the world, and at Selmécbanya in Hungary the mining academy was even offering courses of laboratory instruction at the same period. In Britain, despite its industrial revolution largely based upon coal, and its network of canals, there was no school of mines and no public body responsible for geological surveys until the 1830s.

In 1832 De la Beche's offer to supply geological information to the Ordnance Survey, engaged upon a slow and laborious mapping of the British Isles, was accepted; and soon he succeeded in getting his work recognised as a subsidiary part of the Survey, with a staff of surveyors under his control. He then managed — being very careful never to propose schemes which might seem grandiose or visionary — to get government support for a museum of practical geology; which subsequently moved to a new building in Jermyn Street, where there was a laboratory and where courses of lectures were also given from 1851, when it was opened by Prince Albert. The most eminent palaeontologist working for the Survey at this period was Edward Forbes; he later moved to the Chair of Natural History at Edinburgh — which did not have a Chair of Geology at all until Murchison founded one in 1871 — where he died in middle age. The publications of the Geological Survey are, like those of equivalent bodies abroad, full of palaeontological material; and De la Beche's own publications, such as the *Geological Observer* (1851), also contain some plates of characteristic fossils, although palaeontology was not his main interest. De la Beche's school of mines now forms part of Imperial College in London, and his museum — over which Murchison later presided — is also in South Kensington.

The comparative anatomist to whom the fossils were passed on by the geologist was interested in them not only to identify them so as to identify strata, but also as organic remains of a former world, as clues enabling him to study extinct creatures and thereby perhaps to cast light on the structures and affinities of living creatures. The great names in this borderline territory in the generation after Cuvier were Agassiz and Owen. Even before he graduated

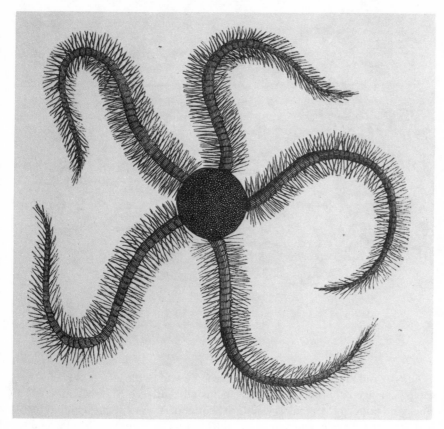

from Munich in 1830 Agassiz had published a report of fish collected in Brazil
by Spix and Martius; he soon made himself one of the leading authorities on
the classification of fish. He pointed out the importance of the character and
structure of the scales — a factor relatively neglected by Cuvier and Valenciennes — and distinguished fish into four great groups, the *Placoids, Ganoids,
Ctenoids,* and *Cycloids*. Like any system based upon one character, this was
bound to be artificial; Günther affirmed that Agassiz would have recognised
this shortcoming himself if he 'had had an opportunity of acquiring a more
extensive and intimate knowledge of existing fishes before his energies were
absorbed in the study of their fossil remains.' Agassiz's work on fossil fish was
published in five volumes at Neuchâtel between 1833 and 1843; it was a
monumental affair, lavishly illustrated, and of great value to those who were
faced with fossil fish, which are common for instance in the Old Red Sandstone
of Scotland described by Hugh Miller. Fish from the yellow sandstone of Dura
Den in Fife were described by Miller and by Agassiz, and are very strikingly
illustrated in Anderson's *Dura Den* (1859), with tinted lithographs.

171

95
Fossil fish, from Anderson's
Dura Den (1859)

Agassiz called the attention of the learned world to the effects of glaciers as geological agents, something hitherto insufficiently considered; and when Buckland noticed their effects visible in Scotland, Agassiz suggested that there had been an ice age in which much of Europe had been covered by glaciers. In 1851 he went to America, to a post at Harvard; there he wrote four illustrated volumes entitled *Contributions to the Natural History of the United States* (1857–62). His great contemporary Richard Owen went from Lancashire to London as a student at St Bartholemew's hospital; he was soon given a post in the museum of the Royal College of Surgeons, in whose hands was the collection of anatomical specimens assembled by John Hunter. Owen, collaborating with Clift the curator whose son-in-law and successor he was to become, worked over the collection, and published a catalogue of it. He made himself 'the English Cuvier', the greatest authority on comparative anatomy in the country, to whom fossil or recent bones or shells could be sent for a verdict.

Owen's most dramatic achievement was the identification of the moa (or *Dinornis*) of New Zealand from a piece of bone broken at both ends; the task was made more difficult because the bone was not hollow as bird-bones generally are, but was a marrow-bone. He wrote a work on the pearly nautilus; a study of teeth; studies of fossil reptiles, marsupials of Australia, and birds of New Zealand; and a semi-popular work, *Palaeontology*; and all of these were

172

handsomely illustrated. His *British Fossil Reptiles* he said cost £1,000 to print, of which the British Association contributed £250; he was having an edition of 350 printed, and reckoned to cover his costs when he had sold 200. The British Association voted £200 for another of Owen's works, and he received various royalties; yet he could assure the income tax authorities in the 1870s that he received no net income from his publications. He received a grant from the government of New South Wales to publish his work on Australian marsupial fossils in separate form; and helped to organise a government grant to enable Falconer to publish an account of the fossils he had found in the Sewalik Hills in India; but such grants only covered costs, and were not intended to be an income.

Agassiz deserves to be remembered here as the compiler of a magnificent and very useful index of zoological publications, which was edited by H. E. Strickland and published by the Ray Society in four volumes between 1848 and 1854; he and Owen were much more than two of the most prominent opponents of Darwin and Huxley in the 1860s. Owen had published a book on archetypes in 1848, and Agassiz an *Essay on Classification* in 1857; both were strongly impressed by the homologies found in the animal kingdom, but they preferred to see them simply as given. They therefore found Darwin's theory hypothetical and unscientific. Both were also given to rhetoric of a religious

96
Fossil jaws, from Falconer's
Palaeontological Memoirs
(1868)

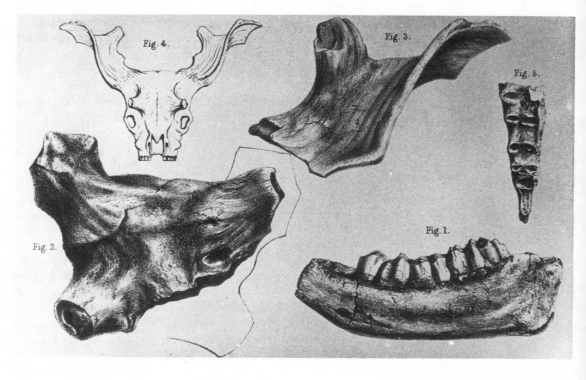

173

kind, and were in fact religious men; but it is wrong to suppose that they and their contemporaries who did not accept evolution by natural selection clung instead to a theory of special creations. Some may have done so; but most preferred to take the various sorts of creatures as given, and to get on with the real job of classifying them and understanding how they fitted, or had fitted, into their environment. This feeling was especially strong among those who, like Owen and Agassiz, were essentially laboratory and museum zoologists, rather than field naturalists who are likely to be more impressed by the struggle for existence. The point was not that there were two theories of the origin of species, but that one could argue whether such a theory was possible; it was urged that the concern of science was not with the origins of things but with their relationships — Newton after all had not written about the creation of the solar system, but only of the laws governing the motions of planets.

Darwin's theory gave a new impetus to palaeontology, because if one accepted it — perhaps only as a working hypothesis — one perforce had to accept the imperfection of the geological record. The establishment of the evolutionary histories of species became the great problem facing the palaeontologist; for in 1859 there was no species for which such a reasonably clear and full history could be given — having seen the hypothetical genealogies set out in the anonymous *Vestiges* (1844) Darwin resolved not to risk any himself. Owen described the toothed bird *Archæopteryx*, found in a lithographic-stone quarry in Germany, in 1863, thus casting light upon the ancestry of the great group of creatures; while in America the fossil history of the horse was worked out by Cope, and that of birds filled in by his great rival Marsh — the two competing with the ruthlessness and expense of industrial tycoons for the fossil riches of the West.

It is always a good plan to outlive one's opponents, and when T. H. Huxley survived Owen, with whom he had had various clashes, he wrote a chapter on Owen's science to go in the standard biography written by Owen's grandson. One might remark in passing that such works are rarely very exciting to read, but they do usually contain a bibliography of their subject's writings and sometimes reproduce illustrations from his work; and that it is a useful corrective to a whiggish view of scientific progress to read such *Lives* of those who, like Owen and Sedgewick, were on what might be described as the wrong side in some great debate. After praising Owen's memoirs on comparative anatomy, Huxley went on to criticise his work on archetypes, and to present a view of Owen as essentially old-fashioned, an anatomist in the eighteenth-century tradition, who had never appreciated the new physiology developed in France and subsequently in Germany. He referred especially to the work of von Baer on embryology, and of Müller in physiology, suggesting that to understand their work, knowledge of the physical sciences was necessary.

Owen was part of the first generation in Britain who seem to have been at home with the microscope, and was indeed one of the founders in 1840 of the

Royal Microscopical Society. It is well-known that Darwin never felt at home with the compound microscope, and was pleased when his children could do microscopical observations for him. When Schleiden's *Scientific Botany* was translated into English in 1849 it included an appendix of sixteen pages on how to use a microscope; it is astonishing that this should have been necessary in an advanced work, but we might remember that on Tuckey's ill-fated expedition to the Zaire (1816) none of the naturalists appointed by the Royal Society (who included a Danish professor) could draw specimens seen through a microscope. It is perhaps not surprising that those who felt daunted by microscopes should not have felt at home in a laboratory with chemical apparatus. Medical students did have to learn chemistry, and increasing emphasis was placed upon it after the founding of the University of London in the 1830s; but before that time little was required, and laboratory instruction was rarely given. In classification, the bones and skins of animals were studied; but Edward Forbes said in jest that some of those classifying (and the same might have been said for drawing) animals did not know that under the skin they had not always been stuffed with straw.

Just as chemists have always been suspicious that physicists are anxious to 'reduce' their science by explaining in principle the affinity of particles, so biologists have looked askance at chemists who seem keen to reduce animals to collections of biochemical mechanisms, and regard everything else as stamp-collecting. In the late eighteenth century, John Hunter in his work on self-digestion (which does not happen in life) seemed to have demonstrated that the ordinary laws of chemistry were not enough to account for physiological processes; and his disciple Brodie's studies in 'respiration' in a dead rabbit showed that this did not generate body-heat although some of the oxygen pumped into the lungs was apparently converted into carbon dioxide. Even to the chemist Humphry Davy at the end of his life in 1829, it seemed that matter in the living body obeyed new laws.

This view was contested by Prichard, who argued in 1829 against the doctrine of a vital principle as unintelligible or unnecessary. He became famous as the leading ethnologist of his day, and was a firm insister upon the unity of mankind, as befitted an evangelical opponent of the slave trade. Indeed, later in the century Darwinian theory, in denying the gulf that separated all men from all animals, could be used to provide some support for the belief that some men were closer to apes than others, and hence in the rightness of negro slavery; it was no accident that it should have been Bishop Wilberforce (a son of William Wilberforce) who appeared as the champion of Darwin's opponents. Prichard wrote a handsomely-illustrated work on the *Natural History of Man* (1843); this publication reminds us that in the first half of the nineteenth century man was still treated as a zoological species, even though one set at a distance from other species. The collection of human skulls for comparative purposes had been going on since the late eighteenth century, when Blumenbach had built up a collection at Göttingen; Humboldt and other travellers picked up skulls on their travels, along with other specimens of natural history.

Huxley had himself brought notice of von Baer's work to his benighted compatriots when he translated 'Fragments relating to Philosophical Zoology' in the journal *Scientific Memoirs* for 1853. This useful publication existed to translate into English memoirs in other languages, especially German; there were seven volumes altogether, appearing between 1837 and 1853, the first five covering the whole range of sciences while the last two are divided so that one is assigned to natural philosophy and the other to natural history. Embryological observations brought to light relationships between animals, and disposed of some theories favoured by comparative anatomists such as the vertebral theory of the skull, which held that it was homologous with a number of vertebrae. The word 'evolution' appears in nineteenth-century discussions of embryology in a sense different from that which it later came to convey; it meant simply the growth of an organism from apparently undifferentiated matter, and not the development of species out of less highly-organised ones, and it was for this reason that the word does not appear in the early editions of the *Origin of Species*.

Johannes Müller was the greatest physiologist of the first half of the nineteenth century, and his pupils at the University of Berlin included many of the greatest of the next generation, such as Helmholtz, Schwann, Virchow, and Du Bois Reymond. Müller's work formed the basis for the classification of fishes in the second half of the century; another of his pupils, Albert Günther, came to Britain and worked at the British Museum, where in the end he became Keeper of Zoology and established himself as the leading ichthyologist of his day. His works on fishes and reptiles were beautifully illustrated by G. H. Ford, and the illustrations of, for example, the *Fishes of Zanzibar* (1866) are unsurpassed. Müller's work also led to improvements in the classification of birds, for he examined their vocal organs and wrote a memoir about them. This was highly praised by Alfred Newton in his famous and indipensable *Dictionary of Birds* (1893–7), which was itself illustrated with wood engravings from Swainson's *Natural History and Classification of Birds* (1836–7), for although Swainson's classification soon seemed eccentric to successors his pictures continued to set a standard; there are, however, some places where Newton had to use newer pictures, especially where he wanted something more like a diagram.

Newton's *Dictionary* begins with a long general essay, and is then organised like an encyclopedia in alphabetical order. Since the eighteenth century, encyclopedias had been handsomely illustrated, and some had been set out such that one could actually use them for learning rather than for reference — though one should bear in mind the remark of Opie the painter: 'Depend upon it, a self-taught person is a person taught by a very ignorant man.' The

97 Illustrations by Ford for the *Fishes of India*, by Günther's arch-rival, Francis Day (1875–78) — note the fine detail in the lithography

Encyclopedia Metropolitana was the great example of a 'philosophical' work; for it began with two volumes of treatises on the pure sciences, followed by six on the 'mixed' or empirical sciences, then five on history, then twelve in alphabetical order, and finally three volumes of plates. The fifth volume of mixed sciences contains book-length articles on botany, zoology, and the medical sciences; and there are excellent engravings in large quarto size, some by Mrs Withers the well-known botanical artist, others by Havell, J. D. C. Sowerby, Charles Landseer, and other artists. The plan for the great work had been drawn up by Coleridge; but the problem with such an encyclopedia was that it was very hard to revise as its classification of knowledge became obsolete — which had happened by the time the final volumes came out, because the enterprise took nearly thirty years.

Other encyclopedias of the eighteenth and nineteenth centuries are useful sources (often neglected) for zoological illustrations; these include the great French works, the *Encyclopédie* of Diderot and D'Alembert and the later *Encyclopédie Méthodique* and in Britain, the *Encyclopedia Britannica*, which went through a steady succession of editions. To those editions in the middle of the nineteenth century, there was appended a volume of dissertations on the progress and present state of knowledge; this is a useful general guide. The ninth and tenth editions, (the latter being the ninth with ten extra volumes and an index) are particularly valuable and authoritative; and because of the way they are organised, it is very easy to see the change in a field between 1875, when the ninth edition came out, and 1902 when the extra volumes making up the tenth were published. In general, the series of editions enable us to follow changes in theory, typography, and illustration over a long period; and it is a pity that these often attractive series of illustrations are immured in such series of dusty and unwieldy tomes, where the topics are in alphabetical rather than systematic order. About the middle of the nineteenth century, the engravings gave way to wood-engravings set in with the text, producing a revolution in the appearance of the volumes because the plates had previously appeared separately; whilst this brought gains in clarity and usefulness, it brought aesthetic losses.

Rees' *Cyclopedia* was another famous work of the second decade of the nineteenth century, with very eminent contributors; these were not identified by initials as they are in later *Encyclopedia Britannicas*, though there is a general list of contributors in the Introduction to the massive work. The date is given as 1819–20, but parts had appeared earlier; B. D. Jackson, in 1895, published a bibliographical study of the work. Similar in title but very different in fact was the *Cabinet Cyclopedia* of Dionysius Lardner, which was really a series of books in uniform format (octavo) covering much of the spectrum of knowledge. Lardner was supposed to have changed his name from the less-exotic Dennis; because he bullied eminent men into undertaking books for the series and into keeping their deadlines, and because his assumed name was that of a

98 Plate, including dissections, from Blackwall's *Spiders* (1861–64)

Sicilian despot, he was called 'the tyrant'. His bullying paid off in that he got John Herschel to write a *Preliminary Discourse* (1830) on scientific methodology, which was greatly admired by contemporaries including Darwin; Swainson wrote another *Preliminary Discourse* (1834), on the study of natural history, which while less authoritative in its day is still interesting, and also a curious compilation called *Taxidermy, bibliography and biography*, which is at once practical advice and history.

Lardner's series was not particularly directed towards natural history, but Jardine's *Naturalists' Library* was, and is a valuable and beautiful collection of little books with hand-coloured plates. Artists included Lear and Swainson, whose volume on *Flycatchers* (1838) is notorious on account of its excellent illustrations and idiosyncratic text, which is set out following the quinary system. Each of the volumes contains a biography of some great naturalist from the past, recent or remote, who interested himself in the creatures discussed and depicted in the volume. Among the authors in the series was William Macgillivray, who wrote on *British Quadrupeds* (1838), and who — as is particularly shown in his *History of British Birds* (1837–52) — based his classifications firmly upon anatomical investigations; but the general impression of the series is that it is a little old-fashioned when one remembers what physiologists like Müller were doing at the same time.

In 1844 the Ray Society was inaugurated, with founder members including Jardine, Owen, Edward Forbes, and Thomas Bell; the object of the Society was the promotion of natural history by the printing of original, newly-edited, or translated works on botany and zoology. The series continues to the present, and includes a large number of zoological works; the majority are systematic studies on the British fauna, but some are more general, one of the most famous being Darwin's study of barnacles (1851–4). The books varied in size, but most are large octavos; exceptions are Nitzsch's *Pterylography* of 1867 which is a large quarto, and is concerned with the distribution of feathers in different kinds of birds; and Blackwell's *Spiders of Great Britain* (1861–4). Nitzsch's editor wrote of plate 1 in *Pterylography* that the author had been unable to decide whether to draw an actual feather to illustrate the parts, or to draw a diagram; in the event, the plate was drawn 'chiefly from nature'. The Ray Society's volumes are generally illustrated, and the books are handsome as well as useful; but they are technical studies — several early ones were translated from the German, in which the new physiological biology was appearing — and aim at clarity rather than at beauty. Many of them are concerned with dissected creatures, so that while the non-expert might admire the accuracy of the line and the delicacy of the printing, he is unlikely to be tempted to vandalise the book in order to frame the plates.

The Ray Society's volumes did not constitute a journal; rather it was a society which published books for which there was a definite market of subscribers. This method of publishing was a valuable nineteenth-century

99   Crow hybrids, from Seebohm's *Birds of Siberia* (1901)

invention, and there were other societies which did the same — notably the Hakluyt Society, which publishes narratives of travel many of which contain valuable observations of natural history. By the 1830s there were many journals publishing illustrated papers on zoology, and the number increased during the century. Some of these newer journals had short lives, like Macgillivray's *Edinburgh Journal of Natural History* which ran from 1835 to 1840; others were more successful, like the *Zoological Record* which was begun by Günther and Newton in 1864 and was eventually taken over by an association of subscribers. In 1859 the British Ornithological Union had begun to publish its journal, *The Ibis*; between 1876 and 1883 the corresponding American publication, *The Auk*, began, and these were later joined by the Australian journal, *The Emu*, and the New Zealand one, *Notornis*. The *Transactions* and *Proceedings* of the Zoological Society of London were illustrated by distinguished artists, including Wolf, Keulemans, Smit and Grönvold; and excellent zoological plates sometimes appeared also in journals like *The Field*, *The National Geographic Magazine*, and *Forest and Stream*.

The physiological and Darwinian revolutions of the mid nineteenth century did not extinguish beautifully-illustrated zoological work, though they did mean that such books were no longer generally seen as of fundamental scientific importance and therefore had to be justified to a greater extent than before on aesthetic grounds. The physiological revolution meant that much of the most intellectually exciting work was being done in laboratories by scientists who had a training in physics and chemistry rather than in medicine, geology, or natural history; their publications were illustrated, if at all, with diagrams or with drawings made through a microscope rather than with what one normally thinks of as zoological pictures. The camera did clear up certain anatomical points about motion, and led to further demands on the zoological artist that he portray animals in lifelike positions, even if these do sometimes have the curious frozen look of high-speed photographs. Work on genetics did not again have a powerful direct effect on zoological art, though one might notice Seebohm's illustration of hooded and carrion crows, with hybrids between these forms.

The Darwinian revolution scarcely affected taxonomists, for it made little difference whether natural groups were simply thought of as 'given', or were seen as having a common ancestor; but the Darwinian theory did help to provide a programme for the palaeontologist. Darwin was not only important in giving an historical perspective in biology; his theory also raised questions that could only be answered by observation of living creatures in the field, and therefore helped to revive the natural history side of biology. The division among biologists into ecologists and physiologists in effect goes back about one hundred years, as the promised lands seen by Müller and by Darwin were occupied by their disciples.

Animal colouration was one of the points that suddenly seemed to need

100
A field naturalist, from
Newman's *History of Insects*
(1841)

some explanation. In his *Illustrations of the Eggs of British Birds* of 1846, Hewitson suggested that they were often bright-coloured to delight the eye of man; but Darwin reinforced Aristotle's belief that no species will have developed some attribute for the good of another. Unless any characteristic had value in the struggle for existence, it would have disappeared, or like the appendix in man be in the process of disappearing. Bates, as a result of his travels on the Amazon with Wallace between 1848 and 1859, hit upon the idea that harmful or unpleasant insects might be so coloured as to warn off predators, and that some harmless and tasty species might 'mimic' them; he thus opened up a whole field for investigation, for colour was suddenly something fundamental instead of merely an aid to recognising a species.

In 1892 F. E. Beddard published his book on *Animal Coloration*, which had grown out of lectures given at the London Zoo. The book contained plates by Smit, the well-known zoological illustrator, which were reproduced by chromo-lithography; they therefore have the slightly muddy tone characteristic of the plates of this period. In America, Abbott Thayer wrote various papers on protective colouration from the 1890s on, his work being summed up in his son Gerald's *Concealing-coloration in the Animal Kingdom* (1909); Thayer's

183

101   Mimicry among butterflies, from a paper by Bates, *Transactions of the Linnean Society, 23* (1861)

theories involved him in a clash with the big-game hunting President, Theodore Roosevelt. Thayer was a painter by training, and a natural historian by inclination; he was struck by the way patterns of colours of animals and birds are so arranged that they are very hard to see against their background — indeed, it is as if they were transparent — especially when they are doing dangerous things like sitting on a nest. He showed that animals are coloured darkest where they are most exposed to sunlight, and palest where they are least exposed; thus their backs are usually darker than their bellies, so that in sunlight an animal's outline disappears. During the First World War, Thayer tried — at first unsuccessfully — to get the Army authorities in Britain and the USA to follow the methods used by animals in camouflaging ships and vehicles.

Thayer's greatest convert was Louis Agassiz Fuertes, who by his name was presumably intended from birth to be a zoological artist. Fuertes showed birds against actual backgrounds not merely for the sake of adding local colour to what might otherwise be a rather dull picture, but to indicate how their colour tones fitted in with those of their surroundings. This is something that is quite hard to do, for some of Thayer's paintings do look almost like puzzle-pictures reminding one of 'Mr. One-Two-Three-Where's-your-Breakfast' in the *Just-so Stories*. One does want to be able to identify the subject of a zoological illustration, even if it is difficult to do so in the depths of the forest where the creature lives. Fuertes died young in 1924; many of his best pictures were done for Oberholser who was working for the U.S. Bureau of Biological Survey on an account of *The Bird Life of Texas*; Oberholser kept accumulating further information, and the book only saw the light of day in 1974, a decade after his death, with a severely-pruned though still very full text, and with Fuertes' illustrations.

Fuertes and Thayer were not the first to perceive protective colouration, although they made more of it than most; the best zoological artists, who had studied animals in the field as well as the museum, had succeeded in reproducing it even if they had not been fully aware of its significance. During the second half of the nineteenth century, the backgrounds of animal and bird pictures had steadily become fuller; Barraband's and some of Siebold's are simply painted on white paper, the backgrounds in Gould's plates steadily assumed more importance through his working life, and in the lithographs and chromolithographs of the late nineteenth century there seem to be no vacant spaces left. No doubt part of the explanation is accounted for by what we would consider a Victorian taste for ornament and clutter; but there was also a Darwinian conviction that animals after all live in the country and not in museums.

Species were seen by Darwinians as filling an ecological niche; that is, they occupied a definite habitat, and depended upon definite sources of food. These were things that could be indicated in a plate; and indeed sometimes had been

185

102
**Plate by Keulemans in
Buller's** *Birds of New Zealand*
(1888 edn)

in illustrations from previous centuries, where a birds is for example shown in
a tree with its prey. Variation among wild animals suddenly became a matter
of interest; in museums where there were relatively few specimens of any one
species variation had not been as apparent as it was to breeders of pigeons or
prize pigs; Darwin and Wallace suddenly made the extent of variation in the
wild a matter of great interest, because there had to be variation for natural
selection to work on. Zoological artists might be expected to indicate the range
of variety found within a species — of size and colour for instance. Artists had
always been expected to show the creatures they painted in lifelike and

186

characteristic positions; but again Darwin's theory of sexual selection made aspects of behaviour particularly interesting — artists had to decide whether to show the animal doing some extraordinary and interesting display, or going about its ordinary business as one would normally see it.

The recognition of living animals and birds was something that became of much greater scientific importance with the new interest in populations, distribution, and migration; and the advent of binoculars by the end of the nineteenth century made such observation possible. Many of the great bird or animal books, showing every feather or whisker as one would see them if one found oneself a yard away from an osprey or a tiger sitting peacefully down, were of little value for identifying a species only fleetingly seen. A new kind of illustration was needed for the field guides which have been a feature of natural history in the twentieth century, helping one to recognise creatures seen in the

103

Cockatoo head, from **F. H. H.** Guillemard, *Cruise of the Marchesa* (1889 edn)

wild and emphasising points that separate the species from others even though these may not be very significant in taxonomy.

The big illustrated books were thus something that one consulted at home or in a library, to see the details of the creature one had seen and identified but whose life one had spared — for bloodless natural history has fortunately become the norm in the twentieth century. The picture therefore has to be accurate; and altogether the demands made upon the zoological artist in the last hundred years have been very high; their life is no easier, even though they have a greater range of media and of printing techniques than their predecessors had. The most notable work of the late nineteenth century was Lord Lilford's *British Birds* in seven volumes (1885–97); Lilford was very fastidious and chose the team of artists to illustrate this work with great care, so that it is a great monument to the zoological artists of the period. The major contributor of plates was Archibald Thorburn, who managed to depict birds in an astonishingly lifelike manner, and his plates are often reproduced; his own *British Birds* (1915–16) was printed photographically, and is therefore perhaps less attractive than Lilford's volumes. The last hand-coloured lithographed bird book to be published in Britain was Mathews' *Birds of Australia* (1910–27), with supplementary volumes on Norfolk Island down to 1936; the artists chiefly responsible for these were Grönvold, Frohawk and Keulemans.

Wolf, whose success in capturing birds in fleeting but not frozen-looking positions was unrivalled, also painted animals; for instance in Sclater and Thomas' *Book of Antelopes* (1894–1900), in which others of the plates were done by Keulemans. J. G. Millais' *Mammals of Great Britain and Ireland* (1904–6) was another fine illustrated work on this group of animals; and Thorburn also published a book on *British Mammals* (1920–1). Since that time the painting and sketching (for sketches can sometimes be better than finished paintings when it comes to identifying a wild creature) of zoological species has still continued. Even if zoological illustration is less important to the working scientist than it was, partly because emphases have changed and partly because there is now a good stock of illustration done by our ancestors, it is still true that a good picture can tell us more than a page of text. We can see this from the way in which illustrations from the past have outlived their text; but one must remember that while the best pictures thus live on, there are no definitive zoological pictures. The interests and needs of each generation are very different from those of its predecessors, and hence the demands made of its zoological artists are different. We are fortunate in our own day that there is no lack of such people, producing the whole range of zoological art from sumptuous folios like those of Morris to field guides and to the diagrams in zoological textbooks and physiological works; and we are equally fortunate in having printers capable of reproducing these to a standard worthy of the great tradition of zoological art, so as to convey both pleasure and knowledge.

Bibliography

Adams, A.(ed), *Zoology of the Voyage of HMS Samarang*, 1848–50
Agassiz, L., *Les Poissons Fossiles*, 5 vols + atlas, Neuchâtel 1833–43; supplement 1844–5;
  Monographie d'Échinodermes, Neuchâtel 1838–42;
  Histoire Naturelle des Poissons d'Eau Douce, 2 vols. + atlas, Neuchâtel 1839–42;
  Les Mollusques Fossiles, 4 vols, Neuchâtel 1840–5;
  Contributions to the Natural History of the USA, 4 vols, Boston 1857–62
[Aitken], E. H., *The Tribes on my Frontier*, Bombay 1883
Alpheraky, S. N., *The Geese of Europe and Asia*, J. Marshall (tr.), 1905
Amuchástegui, A., *Birds and Mammals of South America*, 1967
Anderson, J., D. D., *Dura Den*, Edinburgh 1859
Anderson, J., *The Expedition to Western Yunnan*, Calcutta 1871;
  Mandalay to Momien, 1876;
  Anatomical and Zoological Researches, 2 vols, 1878;
  Zoology of Egypt, 3 vols, 1898–1907
Annals (and Magazine) of Natural History, 1(1837)–; the *Magazine of Nat. Hist.* joined with the *Annals* in 1841
Anon, *A Sketch of the History of Monkeys*, 1848
Antelme, A., *Histoire Naturelle des Insectes et des Mollusques*, 2 vols, Paris 1841
Archer, G., and Goodman, E. M., *Birds of British Somaliland*, 4 vols 1937–61
The Auk, 1(1876)–
Back, G., *Narrative of the Arctic Land Expedition*, 1836
Baird, S. F., *Mammals of North America*, Philadelphia 1857–9;
  The Birds of North America, Philadelphia, 1860
Baird, S. F., *et al.*, *A History of North American Birds*, 3 vols., Boston, 1874
Baird, W., *The British Entomostraca*, 1850
Baker, E. C. S., *The Indian Ducks*, 1908;
  Indian Pigeons and Doves, 1913;
  The Game Birds of India, Burma and Ceylon, 2 vols, 1921;
  Birds of British India, 8 vols, 1922–30
Balfour, F. M., *Comparative Embryology*, 2 vols, 1880–81;
  Works, 4 vols, 1885
Bannerman, D. A., *Birds of the British Isles*, 12 vols, 1953–63;
  Birds of the Atlantic Isles, 4 vols, 1963–68
Bartlett, E. A., *The Weaver-birds*, 1888–89
Bate, C. S., and Westwood, J. O., *British Sessile-eyed Crustacea*, 2 vols, 1863–68
Bates, H. W., *The Naturalist on the River Amazons*, 2 vols, 1863
Beavan, R., *Handbook of the Freshwater Fishes of India*, 1877
Beddard, F. E., *Animal Coloration*, 1892;
  A Book of Whales, 1900
Beebe, C. W., *Two Bird-lovers in Mexico*, Boston 1905;
  The Bird, Its Form and Function, New York 1906;
  A Monograph of the Pheasants, 4 vols, 1918–22;
  Pheasants, their Lives and Homes, New York 1926
Beebe, C. W., *et al.*, *Tropical Wild Life in British Guiana*, New York 1917
Beechey, F. W., *Zoology of the Voyage to the Pacific*, 1839
Bell, T., *British Quadrupeds*, 1837;
  British Reptiles, 1839;
  British Stalk-eyed Crustacea, 1853

Bendire, C., *Life Histories of North American Birds*, 2 vols, Washington 1892–95

Benenden, P. J. van, *Animal Parasites and Messmates*, 1876

Berge, F., *Die Fortpflanzung Europäischer . . . Vögel*, 2 vols, Stuttgart 1840–41;
  Schmetterlingsbuch, Stuttgart 1842;
  Käferbuch, Stuttgart 1844

Bernard, H. M., *The Apodidae*, 1892

Blackburn, H., *Birds Drawn from Nature*, Edinburgh 1862;
  Birds from Moidart, Edinburgh 1895

Blackwell, J., *Researches in Zoology*, 1834;
  Spiders of Great Britain and Ireland, 1860–64

Blandford, W. T., *Geology and Zoology of Abyssinia*, 1870

Blandford, W. T., *et al.*, (eds.), *The Fauna of British India*, 1888–; since 1950 the *British* has been omitted

Bleeker, P., *Atlas Ichthyologique des Indes Orientales*, 9 vols, Amsterdam 1862–78

Blyth, E., and Tegetmaier, W. B., *Natural History of the Cranes*, 1881

Bombay Natural History Society, *Journal*, 1(1886)–

Booth, E. T., *Rough Notes on Birds in the British Islands*, 2 vols, 1881–87

Boston Society of Natural History, *Journal*, 1(1834)–7(1863); *Proceedings*, 1(1841)–;
  Memoirs, 1(1866)–; *Occasional Papers*, 1(1869)–

Boulenger, E. G., *Reptiles and Batrachians*, 1913

Boulenger, G. A., *Tailless Batrachians of Europe*, 2 vols, 1897–98

Bowerbank, J. S., *The British Spongiadae*, 4 vols, 1864–82

Brady, G. S., *Free and Semi-parasitic Copepoda of the British Islands*, 3 vols, London 1878–80

Brasher, R., *Birds and Trees of North America*, 12 vols, Kent, Connecticut 1930

British Association, *Report*, 1(1831–2)–

Buckland, F. T., *Curiosities of Natural History*, 4 vols, 1858–66
  The Curious World of Frank Buckland, by G. H. O. Burgess, 1968

Buckler, W., *Larvae of the British Butterflies and Moths*, 9 vols, 1886–1901

Buckton, G. B., *The British Aphides*, 4 vols, 1876–83;
  The British Cicadae, 2 vols, 1890–91

Buller, W. L., *The Birds of New Zealand*, 1873; 2nd edn, 1887; new edn, 1967

Butler, A. G., *Foreign Finches in Captivity*, 1894;
  British Birds with their Nests and Eggs, 6 vols, 1896–98

Cambridge Natural History, S. F. Harmer and A. E. Shipley (eds.), 10 vols, 1895–1909

Cambridge, O. P., *The Spiders of Dorset*, Sherborne 1879–81

Cameron, P., *The British Phytophagous Hymenoptera*, 4 vols, 1882–93

Carlson, K. L., and Binford, L. C., *Birds of Western North America*, New York 1974

Carpenter, W. B., *Zoology*, 2 vols, 1857–58

Carus, J. V. (ed.), *Icones Zootomicae*, Leipzig 1857

Caton, J. D., *The Antelope and Deer of America*, New York 1877

Catton, C., *Animals Drawn from Nature*, 1788

Cheshire, F. R., *Bees and Bee-keeping*, 2 vols, 1886–88

The Condor, 1(1899)–

Cotton, J., *Birds of the Port Phillip District of NSW, 1843–9*, A. McEvey (ed.), 1974

Coues, E., *Key to North American Birds*, Salem 1872

Cramp, S., and Simmons, K. E. L., *Handbook of the Birds of Europe*, Oxford 1977–

Cuvier, G. F., *Des Dents des Mammiferes*, Strasburg 1825;
  De l'histoire Naturelle des Cetaces, Paris 1836

Cuvier, G. F., and Geoffroy-Saint-Hilaire, E., *Histoire Naturelle des Mammiferes*, 4 vols, Paris [1818]–42

Dalton, S., *Borne on the Wind*, 1975

Dalyell, J. G., *Rare and Remarkable Animals of Scotland*, 2 vols, 1847–48
Darwin, C. R. (ed.), *Zoology of the Voyage of HMS Beagle*, 5 pts, 1838–43;
    A Monograph on the Sub-class Cirripedia, 2 vols, 1851–54;
    The Works . . . an annotated bibliographical handlist, by R. B. Freeman, 2nd edn, 1976;
    Collected Papers, P. H. Barratt (ed.), 2 vols, Chicago 1977
Dawson, J. F., *Geodephaga Britannica*, 1854
Dawson, J. W., *Air Breathers of the Coal Period*, Montreal 1863;
    Life's Dawn on Earth, 1875;
    Fossil Men and their Modern Representatives, 1880
Day, F., *The Fishes of Malabar*, 1865;
    The Fishes of India, 4 pts, 1875–78, supplement 1888;
    The Fishes of Great Britain and Ireland, 8 pts, 1880–84;
    The Fauna of British India, Fishes 1 and 2, 1889
Dean, B., *Fishes, Living and Fossil*, New York 1895
De Kay, J. E., *Zoology of New York*, 6 vols, 1842–44
De la Beche, H. T., *How to Observe: Geology*, 1835;
    Geological Observer, 1851
Dement'ev, G. P., *et al.*, *Birds of the Soviet Union*, A. Birron and Z. S. Cole (tr.), 6 vols,
    Jerusalem 1966–68; original Russian edn, Moscow 1951–54
Denny, H., *Monographia Anoplurorum Britanniae*, 1842
Descourtilz, J. T., *Oiseaux brillans et remarquable du Brésil*, Paris 1835; new edn, Amster-
    dam and Rio de Janeiro 1960;
    Ornithologie Brésilienne, Rio de Janeiro, [1854]
Des Murs, M. A. P. O., *Iconographie Ornithologique*, Paris 1845–49
Diggles, S., *The Ornithology of Australia*, 2 vols, 1866–77
Dixon, C., *Rural Bird Life*, 1880;
    The Nests and Eggs of British Birds, 1894;
    The Game Birds and Wild Fowl of the British Islands, 1895;
    Among the Birds in the Northern Shires, 1900
Dixon, F. (ed.), *The Geology and Fossils . . . of Sussex*, 1850 [1852]
Douglas, J. W., and Scott, J., *The British Hemiptera*, vol. 1 (all published), 1865
Dresser, H. E., *A History of the Birds of Europe*, 9 vols, 1871–96;
    A Monograph of the Meropidae, 1884–86;
    A Monograph of the Coraciidae, Farnborough 1893
Duncan, F. M. (ed.), *Cassell's Natural History*, 6 vols, 1878–82
Ecker, A., *The Anatomy of the Frog*, G. Haslam (tr.), Oxford 1889
Edinburgh Encyclopedia, 18 vols, Edinburgh 1808–30
Elliot, D. G., *The Pittidae*, New York, 1861–63;
    The Tetraoninae, New York, [1864]–5;
    Birds of North America, 2 vols, New York, [1866]–9;
    The Phasianidae, 2 vols, New York, [1870]–2;
    The Paradisedae, 1873;
    The Bucerotidae, 1877–82;
    The Felidae, 1883;
    North American Shore Birds, 1895;
    North American Gallinaceous Game Birds, 1897;
    North American Wild Fowl, New York 1898
Emmons, E., *American Geology*, 2 vols, Albany 1855
Entomological Society, *Transactions*, 1(1836)–;
    History, by S. A. Neave, 1933
Ewart, J. C., *The Penycuik Experiments*, 1899

Eyton, T. C., *History of the Rarer British Birds*, 1836;
  The Anatidae, 1838;
  A History of the Oyster, 1858;
  Osteologia Avium, Wellington 1867, supplement 1869–75
Fabre, J. H. C., *Faune Avignonaise; Insectes Coléoptères*, Avignon 1870
  Souvenirs Entomologiques, 7 series, Paris 1879–1900
Falconer, H., *Palaeontological Memoirs*, 2 vols, 1868
Falconer, H. and Cautley, P. T., *Fauna Antiqua Sivalensis*, 1846–49
Finn, F., *Eggs and Nests of British Birds*, 1910;
  Game Birds of India, Calcutta, 1911;
  Indian Sporting Birds, 1915;
  Bird Behaviour, 1919
Fisher, A. K., *Hawks and Owls of the United States*, Washington 1893
Flanagan, G. L., and Morris, S., *Window into a Nest*, 1975
Flower, W. H., *Osteology of the Mammalia*, 1870;
  The Horse, 1891;
  Essays on Museums, 1898
Flower, W. H. and Lydekker, R., *Introduction to the Study of Mammals*, 1891
Forbes, E., and Hanley, S., *A History of British Mollusca*, 4 vols, 1848–53
Forest and Stream, 1(1873)–
Forshaw, J. M., and Cooper, W. T., *Parrots of the World, Melbourne 1973*
Fowler, W. W., *Coleoptera of the British Islands*, 5 vols, 1887–91, supplement 1913
Fraser, L., *Zoologica Typica*, 1849
Fremont, J., *The Exploring Expedition to the Rocky Mountains*, Washington 1845
Gardener's Chronicle, 1(1841)–
Garrard, G., *History of British Cattle*, 1801
Garrod, A. H., *Collected Scientific Papers*, W. A. Forbes (ed.), 1881
Geoffroy-Saint-Hilaire, I., *Études zoologiques*, Paris 1832;
  Histoire des Anomalies de l'Organisation, 3 vols + atlas, Paris 1832–37;
  Essais de Zoologie Generale, Paris 1841
Geological Society, *Transactions*, 1–5, second series, 1–7 (1811–56);
  Proceedings, 1(1834)–4(1846);
  Quarterly Journal, 1(1845)–
Godart, J. B., *Histoire naturelle des Lepidoptères ou Papillons de France*, 11 vols, Paris [1820]–38, supplement, 4 vols, 1832–42
Goodman, F. du C., *Monograph of the petrels*, 2 vols, 1907–10
Goodman, F. du C., and Salvin, O., *Biologia Centrali-Americana*, 57 vols 1879–1915
Gosse, P. H., *Illustrations of the Birds of Jamaica*, 1849;
  A Manual of Marine Zoology, 2 pts, 1855–56;
  Evenings at the Microscope, 1859;
  British sea-anemones and corals, 1860
  A Bibliography, by R. Lister, Cambridge 1952
Gould, J., *A Century of Birds from the Himalaya mountains*, 1831;
  Birds of Europe, 5 vols, 1832–37;
  The Ramphastidae, 1834–35;
  Icones Avium, 1837–38;
  The Trogonidae, 1838;
  Birds of Australia, 7 vols, 1840–48, supplement 1851–69;
  Mammals of Australia, 3 vols, 1845–63;
  The Trochilidae, 5 vols, 1849–61;
  Birds of Asia, 7 vols, 1850–83;

Birds of Great Britain, 5 vols, 1862–73;
Birds of New Guinea, 5 vols, 1875–88
Analytical Index, by R. B. Sharpe, 1893;
Gould, by A. McEvey, Sydney 1973
Gray, G. R., *Genera of Birds*, 3 vols, 1844–49;
Birds of China, 1871
Gray, J. E., *Illustrations of Indian Zoology*, 2 vols, 1830–35;
Gleanings from the Menagerie and Aviary at Knowsley Hall, 2 vols, Knowsley 1846–50;
Specimens of Fish in the B. M., 3 pts, 1851–56;
A Bibliography, by J. Saunders, 1872
Grey, Viscount, of Falloden, *The Charm of Birds*, 1927
Grote, A. R., *The Noctuidae of North America*, 1882
Günther, A., *Reptiles of British India*, 1864;
An Introduction to the Study of Fishes, Edinburgh 1880
Günther, A., and Playfair, R. L., *The Fishes of Zanzibar*, 1866; new edn, G. S. Myers and
    A. E. Gunther (eds.), Kentfield, California 1971
Guillemard, F. H. H., *The Cruise of the Marchesa*, 1886
Harting, J. E., *British Animals Extinct Within Historic Times*, 1880
Hartmann, C. E. W. R., *Der Gorilla*, Leipzig 1880;
Anthropoid Apes, 1885
Harvard University, Museum of Comparative Zoology, *Memoirs &c*, 1(1864)–
Haughton, S., *Principles of Animal Mechanics*, 1873
Hertwig, O., *Embryology of Man and Mammals*, E. L. Mark (tr.), 1892
Hewitson, W. C., *Illustrations of the Eggs of British Birds*, 2 vols, 1846;
Exotic Butterflies, 5 vols, 1856–76;
New Indian Lepidopterous Insects, Calcutta 1879–88
Hickson, S. J., *A Naturalist in North Celebes*, 1889;
The Fauna of the Deep Sea, 1894
Hincks, T., *British Hydroid Zoophytes*, 2 vols, 1868;
British Marine Polyzoa, 2 vols, 1880
Hinds, R. B., (ed.), *Zoology of the Voyage of HMS Sulphur*, 2 vols, 1844
Hitchcock, E., *The Sandstone of the Connecticut Valley*, Boston 1858
Holbrook, J. E., *North American Herpetology*, 5 vols, Philadelphia 1836–42 (new edn,
    1976)
Houssay, F., *The Industries of Animals*, 1893
Hudson, C. T., and Gosse, P. H., *The Rotifera*, 2 vols + supplement, 1886–89
Hudson, W. H., *The Naturalist in la Plata*, 1892;
British Birds, 1895;
Birds in London, 1898;
Birds in town and village, 1919;
Birds of la Plata, 2 vols, 1920;
A Bibliography, by J. R. Payne, 1977
Hume, A. O., and Marshall, C. H. T., *The Game Birds of India*, 3 vols, Calcutta 1879–81
Humphreys, H. N., *Ocean Gardens*, 1857;
Genera of British Moths, 1860
Humphreys, H. N. and Westwood, J. O., *British Butterflies*, 1841;
British Moths, 2 vols, 1843–45
Huxley, J. S., *The Courtship Habits of the Great Crested Grebe, 1914*, 1968
Huxley, T. H., *Lectures on Comparative Anatomy*, 1864;
The Classification of Animals, 1869;
The Anatomy of Vertebrated Animals, 1871;

The Anatomy of Invertebrated Animals, 1877;
The Crayfish, 1879
Ibis, 1(1859)–
Irby, L. H. L., *Ornithology of Gibraltar*, 1875
James, F. L., *The Unknown Horn of Africa*, 1888
Jardine, W. (ed.), *The Naturalist's Library*, 40 vols, 1834–43
Jeffreys, J. G., *British Conchology*, 5 vols, 1862–69
Jerdon, T. C., *Illustrations of Indian Ornithology*, Madras 1847;
Birds of India, 2 vols, 1862–64; new edn, 1877
Johnston, G., *History of the British Zoophytes*, Edinburgh 1838, supplement (*Sponges & Lithophytes*) 1842;
Introduction to Conchology, 1850
Jones, H., *Bird Paintings*, 1976
Jones, T. R., *The Organisation of the Animal Kingdom*, 1838–41;
The Natural History of Animals, 2 vols, 1845–52
Jordan, D. S., *The Fur Seals and Fur-seal Islands*, 4 vols, Washington 1898–99
Jourdain, F. C. J., *Eggs of European Birds*, 4 pts (all published), 1906–09
Kaup, J. J., *Description des Ossements Fossiles*, 5 pts, Darmstadt 1832–39;
Akten der Urwelt, Darmstadt 1841
Kearton, R., *British Bird's Nests*, 1895
Kent, W. S., *A Manual of the Infusoria*, 2 vols + atlas, 1880–82
Kingsley, C., *Glaucus*, Cambridge 1855;
A Companion to Glaucus, by G. B. Sowerby Jnr, 1858
Kirby, W. E., *Insects: Foes and Friends*, 1898
Kirby, W. F., *European Butterflies and Moths*, 1882 (based on Berge);
Elementary Textbook of Entomology, 1885;
The Order Lepidoptera, 5 vols, 1894–97
Knight, C., *Architecture of Birds*, 1831;
ed. *The Penny Cyclopedia*, 29 vols, 1833–46;
ed. *The English Cyclopedia*, 23 vols, 1854–62;
Pictorial Museum of Animated Nature, 2 vols, [1856–58]
Korschelt, E., and Heider, K., *The Embryology of Invertebrates*, E. L. Mark and W. McM. Woodworth (tr.), 4 vols, 1895–1900
Lambert, T., and Mitchell, A., *Birds of Garden and Woodland*, 1976
Lankester, E. R., *Degeneration*, 1880
Extinct Animals, 1905;
From an Easy Chair, 1908;
Diversions, 1915
Lankester, E. R. (ed.), *A Treatise on Zoology*, 9 vols, 1900–09
Lardner, D. (ed.), *The Cabinet Cyclopedia*, 133 volumes, 1830–39
Lear, E., *Illustrations of the Family of Psittacidae*, 1832; see also J. E. Gray, *Gleanings*, 1846
Legge, W. W., *The Birds of Ceylon*, 2 vols, 1878–80
Leidy, J., *The Extinct Mammalian Fauna of Dakota & Nebraska*, Philadelphia 1869
Lesson, R. P., *Voyage sur la Coquille*, Paris 1829, and in the official *Voyage de la Coquille*, 6 vols, 1826–[39];
Manuel d'Ornithologie, Paris 1828;
Des Mammifères et des Oiseaux Découverts depuis 1788, 10 vols, Paris 1828–37;
Histoire Naturelle des Oiseaux-mouches, Paris 1829–30, supplement (*des Colibris*) 1830–32;
Centurie Zoologique, Paris 1830–32;
Traité d'Ornithologie, Paris 1830–31;

194

Les Trochilidées, Paris 1832–33;
Illustrations de zoologie, Paris 1832–35;
Des Oiseaux de Paradis, Paris 1834–35;
Des zoophytes, Paris 1843
Lewes, G. H., *Sea-side Stories*, Edinburgh 1858
Lilford, Lord (T. L. Powys), *Figures of British Birds*, 7 vols, 1885–97
Linnean Society of New South Wales, *Proceedings*, 1(1875)–
Lloyd, L., *Field Sports of the North of Europe*, 2 vols, 1830;
Scandinavian Adventures, 2 vols, 1854;
Game Birds and Wild Fowl of Sweden, 1867
Low, D., *The Breeds of Domestic Animals of the British Islands*, 2 vols, 1842
Lowe, R. T., *Primitiae Faunae et Florae Maderae*, Cambridge 1831;
A History of the Fishes of Madeira, 1843–60
Lowne, B. T., *The Anatomy and Physiology of the Blow-fly*, 1870, 2nd edn, 1890–2
The Collembola and Thysanura, 1873;
British Wild Flowers, Considered in relation to insects, 1873
Lubbock, J., *Scientific Lectures*, 1879;
Ants, Bees, and Wasps, 1882;
The Beauties of Nature, 1892;
On the Senses, Instincts, and Intelligence of Animals, 1908
Lydekker, R. (ed.), *The Royal Natural History*, 6 vols, 1893–96;
Life and Rock, 1894;
Geographical History of Mammals, Cambridge 1896;
Wild Oxen, Sheep, and Goats, 1898;
Deer of All Lands, 1898;
Great and Small Game of India, 1900;
Great and Small Game of Europe, 1901
Macgillivray, J., *The Voyage of HMS Rattlesnake*, 2 vols, 1852
Macgillivray, W., *A History of British Birds*, 5 vols, 1837–52;
British Quadrupeds, Edinburgh 1845–46;
Natural History of Dee Side and Braemar, 1855 (with E. Lankester)
Magasin de Zoologie, 1(1831)–, after 1838 *Revue et Magasin . . .*
Marsh, O. C., *Odontornithes*, Washington 1880
Matthews, G. M., *Birds of Australia*, 12 vols + 5 supplements 1910–27;
Birds of Norfolk and Lord Howe Islands, 1928, supplement 1936
Meyer, H. L., *Illustrations of British Birds*, 4 vols, 1835–41;
Coloured illustrations of British Birds, 7 vols, 1842–50;
Game Birds [c. 1848]
Meinertzhagen, R., *Nicholl's Birds of Egypt*, 2 vols, 1930;
Birds of Arabia, 1954
Millais, J. G., *Game Birds and Shooting Sketches*, 1892;
British Surface-feeding ducks, 1902;
Mammals of Great Britain and Ireland, 3 vols, 1904–6;
British Game Birds, 1909;
British Diving Ducks, 1913
Miller, H., *The Old Red Sandstone*, Edinburgh 1841;
Footprints of the Creator, Edinburgh 1849;
Testimony of the Rocks, Edinburgh 1857
Millière, P., *Iconographie et Description de Chenilles et Lépidoptères inédits*, 3 vols, Paris 1859–74;
Lépidoptérologie, 2 vols, Paris 1881–82;

Catalogue raisonne des Lépidoptères des Alpes-Maritimes, Paris [1887]

Milne-Edwards, H., *Elémens de Zoologie*, Paris 1834–37;
  Histoire Naturelle des Crustacés, 3 vols + atlas, Paris 1834–40;
  Histoire Naturelle des Corallieres, 3 vols + atlas, Paris 1857–60;
  Histoire Naturelle des Mammiferes, Paris 1868–74

Mivart, St. G., *Man and Apes*, 1873;
  The Common Frog, 1874;
  Dogs, Jackals, Wolves, and Foxes, 1890;
  Birds, 1892;
  The Lories, 1896

Montes, R., de Oca, *Humming Birds and Orchids of Mexico, 1878*, Mexico 1963

Morris, F., *Birds of Prey of Australia*, Melbourne 1973;
  Pigeons and Doves of Australia, Melbourne 1976

Morris, F. O., *History of British Birds*, 6 vols, 1851–57;
  British Butterflies, 1852–53;
  Nests and Eggs of British Birds, 3 vols, 1853–56

Moseley, H. N., *Notes by a Naturalist on the 'Challenger'*, 1879

Müller, J., *Zur Vergleichenden Physiologie*, Leipzig, 1826;
  The Vocal Organs of the Passeres, F. J. Bell (tr.), A. H. Garrod (ed.), Oxford 1878

Murchison, R. I., *The Silurian System*, 1839, new edn (*Siluria*) 1854

Murchison, R. I., *et al.*, *The Geology of Russia in Europe*, 2 vols, 1845

Murray, J., and Thomson, C. W. (eds.), *Report on the Scientific Results of the Voyage of HMS Challenger*, 50 vols, 1880–95

Murray, J. A., *The Avifauna of British India*, 2 vols, 1880–90;
  The Vertebrate Zoology of Sind, 1884

Muybridge, E., *Animal Locomotion*, Philadelphia, 1887;
  Descriptive Zoopraxography, Chicago 1893;
  Animals in Motion, 1899

Naturalist's Library, 40 vols, 1834–43, see Jardine

Nature, 1 (1869–70)–

Newberry, J., *Paleozoic Fishes of North America*, Washington 1889

Newman, E., *The Grammar of Entomology*, 1835, 2nd edn (*History of Insects*) 1841;
  Birdsnesting, 1862;
  British Moths, 1869;
  British Butterflies, 1870–71

Newton, A., *A Dictionary of Birds*, 1893–97

Nicholson, E., *Indian Snakes*, 1870

Nicholson, H. A., *A Manual of Zoology*, 2 vols, 1870;
  A Manual of Palaeontology, 2 vols, 1872;
  The Ancient Life-history of the Earth, 1877;
  Tabulate Corals of the Palaeozoic Period, 1879;
  Natural History in Britain, 1886

Nilsson, S., *Ornithologia Svecica*, Havniae 1817–21;
  Skandinavsk Fauna, 8 vols, Lund 1820–60;
  Illuminerade Figurer till Skandinavens Fauna, 2 vols, Lund 1832–40

Nitzsch, C. L., *Pterylography*, H. Burmeister (ed.), Halle 1840; English tr. 1867

Oberholser, H. C., *The Bird Life of Texas*, E. B. Kincaid (ed.), 2 vols, Austin 1974

Ogilvie-Grant, W. R. A., *The Game Birds*, 2 vols, 1895–97

Olphe-Galliard, L., *Contributions á la Faune Ornithologique de l'Europe Occidentale*, 4 vols, Paris 1884–91

d'Orbigny, A. D., *Voyage dans l'Amerique Méridionale*, 7 vols + 2 atlas, Paris 1835–47

d'Orbigny, A. D., *et al.*, *Histoire Naturelle des Crinoides*, Paris 1840–58;
   Mollusques Vivants et Fossiles, 2 vols, Paris 1845–47;
   Palaeontologie Universelle des Coquilles et des Mollusques, Paris 1845–47
   Palaeontologie Francaise, 24 vols, Paris 1840–94;
d'Orbigny, A. D. (ed.), *Dictionnaire Universel d'Histoire Naturelle*, 16 vols, Paris 1839–49
Ornis, 1(1885)–
Owen, R., *The Pearly Nautilus*, 1832;
   British Fossil Mammals and Birds, 1844–46;
   The Archetype and Homologies of the Vertebrate Skeleton, 1848;
   The Nature of Limbs, 1849;
   British Fossil Reptiles, 4 vols, 1849–84;
   Palaeontology, Edinburgh 1860;
   On the Anatomy of the Vertebrates, 3 vols, 1866–68;
   The Extinct Wingless Birds of New Zealand, 1874;
   The Extinct Mammals of Australia, 2 vols, 1877
Palaeontographical Society, *Monographs*, 1(1848)–
Parry, W. E., *Journal of a Voyage*, 1821, supplement 1824;
   A Second voyage, 2 vols, 1824–25;
   A Third voyage, 1826;
   An Attempt to Reach the North Pole, 1828
Peale, T. R., *U.S. Exploring Expedition*, vol. 8, *Mammalia & Ornithology*, Philadelphia,
   1848; replaced by a volume by J. Cassin, 1858; see Wilkes
Perry, M. C., *Narrative of the Expedition to Japan*, F. L. Hawks (ed.), 3 vols, Washington
   1856;
   Personal Journal, R. Pineau (ed.), Washington 1968
Petherick, J. and B. H., *Travels in Central Africa*, 1869
Phillips, J., *The Geology of Yorkshire*, York 1829;
   The Palaeozoic fossils of Cornwall, 1841
Pictet, F. J., *Histoire des Insectes Néuroptères*, 2 pts, Geneva 1841–45;
   Traité Elementaire de Palaeontologie, 4 vols, Geneva 1844–46;
Pictet, F. J. (ed.), *Materiaux pour Laxpalaeontologie Suisse*, 7 vols + atlas, Geneva 1854–73
Poey y Aloy, F., *Centurie de Lépidoptères de l'Ile de Cuba*, Paris 1832;
   Curso de Zoologia, Habana 1843;
   Enumeratio Piscium Cubensium, Madrid 1875–77;
   Memorias sobre la historia natural de la Isla de Cuba, 2 vols, Habana 1851–58
Power, E., *Small Birds of the New Zealand Bush*, 1970;
   Waders in New Zealand, 1972;
   New Zealand Water Birds, 1974
Prichard, J. C., *The Natural History of Man*, 1843; 3rd edn, 1848
Quoy, J. R. C., and Gaimard, J. P., *Voyages de l'Uranie et la Physicienne, Zoologie*, 2 vols,
   Paris 1824–26;
   Voyage de l'Astrolabe, Zoologie, 4 vols + atlas, Paris 1830–35
Ray Society, *Publications*, 1845–;
   Bibliography, by R. Curle, 1954
Reichenbach, H. G. L., *Deutschlands Fauna*, 2 vols, Leipzig 1837–39;
   Vollständigste Naturgeschichte der Vögel, 13 vols, Dresden 1845–62
Roget, P. M., *Animal and Vegetable Physiology*, 2 vols, 1834
   (Bridgewater Treatise)
Roosevelt, T., *Hunting Trips of a Ranchman*, 1886
Roosevelt, T., *et al.*, *The Deer Family*, 1902
Rosenthal, F. C., *Ichthyotomische Tafeln*, 2 vols, Berlin 1812–26, 2nd edn, 1839

Ross, J. C., *A Voyage to the Antarctic Regions*, 2 vols, 1847
Rothschild, L. W., *The Avifauna of Laysan*, 1893–1900;
  The Genus Casuarinus, 1900;
  Extinct Birds, 1907
Royal Institution, *Proceedings*, 1(1851–4)–
Royal Society of New South Wales, *Journal and Proceedings*, 1(1867)–
Royal Society of Tasmania, *Papers & Proceedings*, 1(1849)–
Royle, J. F., *Illustrations of the Botany and other Branches of the Natural History of the Himalayan Mountains*, 2 vols, 1833–40
Salmonsen, F., and Johansen, G., *The Birds of Greenland*, Copenhagen 1950
Salvin, F. H., and Brodrich, W., *Falconry in the British Isles*, 1855, 2nd edn, 1873
Saunden, H., *Illustrated Manual of British Birds*, 1889, 2nd edn, 1899
Saville-Kent, W., *The Great Barrier Reef of Australia*, 1893;
  The Naturalist in Australia, 1897
Schlegel, H., *Essai sur la Physiognomie des Serpens*, 2 vols + atlas, Amsterdam 1837;
  English tr. 1843;
  Amphibien, 2 vols, Dusseldorf 1837–44;
  Abbildungen aus dem Gebeite der Zoologie, Leiden 1841–51;
  Naturlijke Historie van Nederland, 6 vols, Harlem 1860–78;
  De Vogels van Nederland, 1854–8, van Nederlandsch Indie, 3 vols, Leiden 1863–66
Schultze, L. S., *Zoologische Ergebnisse im Südafrika*, 5 vols, Jena 1908–14
Scientific Memoirs, 1—7, (1837–53)
Sclater, P. L., *A Collection of American Birds*, 1862
Sclater, P. L., and Salvin, O., *Exotic Ornithology*, 1866–69
Sclater, P. L., and Bartlett, E., *The Jacamars and Puffbirds*, 1879–82
Sclater, P. L., and Hudson, W. H., *Argentine Ornithology*, 1888–89
Sclater, P. L., and Thomas, O., *The Book of Antelopes*, 4 vols, 1894–1900
Sclater, W. L., and Sclater, P. L., *The Geography of Mammals*, 1899
Sclater, W. L., and Stark, A. C., *The Fauna of South Africa*, 6 vols (all published), 1900–6
Seebohm, H., *Siberia in Europe*, 1880;
  Siberia in Asia, 1882; new edn of these (*Birds of Siberia*), 1901;
  History of British Birds, 3 vols + atlas, 1883–85;
  Geographical Distribution of the Family Charadriidae, 1887;
  Birds of the Japanese Empire, 1890;
  Eggs of British Birds, R. B. Sharpe (ed.), Sheffield 1896
Seeman, B. C., *The Voyage of HMS Herald*, 2 vols, 1853
Seitz, A., *Les Macrolepidopteres du Globe*, 4 pts, Paris 1911–28
Sharpe, R. B., *A Monograph of the Alcedinidae*, 1868–71;
  A Monograph of the Paradiseidae, 2 vols 1891–8;
  A Monograph of the Turdidae, 2 vols, 1898–1902;
  Sketchbook of British Birds, 1898;
  Wonders of the Bird World, 1898
Sharpe, R. B. (ed.), *Allen's Naturalist's Library*, 16 vols, 1894–95
Shelley, G. E., *The Birds of Egypt*, 1872;
  The Nectariniidae, or Sun Birds, 1876–80;
  The Birds of Africa, 5 vols, 1896–1912
Shuckard, W. E., *The Indigenous Fossil Hymenoptera*, 1837;
  British Entomology, 1839;
  British Bees, 1866
Shuckard, W. E., and Spry, W. J., *The British Coleoptera Delineated*, 1840
Siebold, K. T. E., *Die Süsswasserfische von Mitteleuropa*, Leipzig 1863

Siebold, P. F., *et al.*, *Fauna Japonica*, 6 vols, Leyden 1833–50;
  Mammalia Faunae Japonicae, Leyden 1850
Smith, A., *Illustrations of the Zoology of South Africa*, 4 vols, 1838–49
Smith, C. H., *The Natural History of Dogs*, 2 vols, 1839–40;
  The Natural History of Horses, 1841;
  The Natural History of the Human Species, Edinburgh 1848;
  Introduction to Mammalia, 1842
Smith, H. G., and Kirby, W. F., *Rhopalocera Exotica*, 3 vols, 1887–1902
Smithsonian Institution, *Annual Report*, 1(1847)–;
  Contributions to Knowledge, 1(1848)–
Sowerby, G. B., Jnr, *A Conchological Manual*, 1839;
  Thesaurus Conchylorum, 5 vols, 1842–87;
  Popular British Conchology, 1854;
  Illustrated Index of British Shells, 1859
Sowerby, J. de C., and Lear, E., *Tortoises, Terrapins, and Turtles*, 1872
Staudinger, O., and Schatz, E., *Exotische Schmetterlinge*, 2 vols, Fürth [1884]–92
Stevenson, H., and Southwell, T., *Birds of Norfolk*, 3 vols, 1866–90
Stout, G. D. and Matthiesson, P. Clem, R. V. and Palmer, R. S., *The Shore Birds of North America*, New York 1967
Strzelecki, P. E. de, *Physical Description of New South Wales*, 1845
Stuhlmann, F. L., *Zoologische Ergebnisse im Ost-Afrika*, 2 vols, Berlin 1891–1901
Susemihl, J. C. and E. E., *Abbildungen der Vögel Europas*, Stuttgart 1839–51
Sutherland, P., *Journal of a Voyage in Baffin's Bay*, 1852
Swainson, W., *Zoological Illustrations*, 6 vols, 1820–33;
  Exotic Conchology, 1821–22, new edn 1841;
  The Geography and Classification of Animals, 1835;
  The Natural History and Classification of Birds, 2 vols, 1836–37;
  Birds of Western Africa, 2 vols, Edinburgh 1837;
  Animals in Menageries, 1838;
  Flycatchers, Edinburgh 1838;
  Fishes, Amphibians, and Reptiles, 2 vols, 1838–39;
  Taxidermy, 1840;
  Malacology, 1840;
  The Habits and Instincts of Animals, 1840;
  Birds of Brazil and Mexico, 1841
Swainson, W., and Shuckard, W. E., *The History and Natural Arrangement of Insects*, 1840
Swaysland, W., *Familiar Wild Birds*, 4 vols, 1883–88
Tasmanian Journal of Natural Science, 1(1841)–3(1848)
Tegetmaier, W. B., *The Poultry book*, 1856–57;
  Pigeons, 1868;
  Pheasants, 1873;
Tegetmaier, W. and Sutherland, C. L., *Horses, Asses, Zebras, Mules*, 1895
Temminck, C. J., *Les Pigeons*, Paris 1808–13;
  Histoire Naturelle Générale des Pigeons et des Gallinacés, 3 vols, Amsterdam 1813–15;
  Monographies de Mammalologie, 2 vols, Paris 1821–41
Temminck, C. J. (ed.), *Verhandelingen over de Natuurlijke Geschiednis der Nederlandsche overzeesche bezettingen*, 3 vols, Leiden 1839–45
Temminck, C. J. and de Chartrouse, M. Laugier, *Planches Coloriées d'Oiseaux*, Paris [1820–39]
Tennent, J. E., *Sketches of the Natural History of Ceylon*, 1861
Thayer, G. H. and A. H., *Concealing-coloration in the Animal Kingdom*, New York 1909

Thompson, A. L., *Britain's Birds and their Nests*, 1910;
 Problems of Bird Migration, 1926;
 A New Dictionary of Birds, 1964
Thompson, D'A. W., *On Growth and Form*, Cambridge 1917
Thomson, C. W., *The Depths of the Sea*, 1875;
 The Voyage of the Challenger: the Atlantic, 2 vols, 1877;
Thomson, C. W. (ed.), *Challenger Reports*, see Murray.
Thorburn, A., *British Birds*, 4 vols, 1915–16;
 A Naturalist's Sketch Book, 1919, new edn. 1977;
 British Mammals, 2 vols, 1920–21;
 Game Birds, 1923
Tshudi, J. J., *Untersuchungen über de Fauna Peruana*, 4 pts, St Gallen, 1844–46
Tunnicliffe, C. F., *Shorelands Summer Diary*, 1952
Uehara, Y., Campbell, G. R., and Burnstock, G., *Muscle and its Innervation*, 1976
US Government, *Pacific Railroad Surveys*, 11 vols in 12, Washington 1853–59;
 Geological Exploration of the 40th parallel, 7 vols + atlas, 1870–80;
 Geographical and Geological Surveys West of the 100th meridian, 7 vols + atlas, 1874–79;
 Geological & Geographical Survey of the Territories, Catalogue & Index of Publications, Washington 1904;
 Bibliography of American Economic Entomology (Department of Agriculture), 7 pts, Washington 1889–1901
Wallace, A. R., *The Amazon and Rio Negro*, 1853;
 The Malay Archipelago, 1869;
 The Geographical Distribution of Animals, 1876;
 Island Life, 1880
Walton, E., *The Camel*, 1865
Waterhouse, C. O., *Aids to the Identification of Insects*, 2 vols, 1880–90
Waterhouse, G. R., *Marsupalia*, Edinburgh 1841;
 The Mammalia, 2 vols (all published) 1846–48
Werner, J. C., *Atlas des Oiseaux d'Europe*, 4 vols, Paris 1842
Westwood, J. O., *Arcana Entomologica*, 2 vols, 1841–45;
 Cabinet of Oriental Entomology, 1847–48; see also Humphreys
Wetmore, A., *The Migrations of Birds*, 1927
Whitehead, J., *Exploration of Mount Kina Balu*, 1893
Whittaker, J. I. S., *Birds of Tunisia*, 1905
Wilkes, C. *et al.*, *United States Exploring Expedition*, 20 vols, Philadelphia 1845–76
Williston, S. W., *American Permian Vertebrates*, Chicago 1911;
 Water Reptiles of the Past and Present, Chicago, 1914;
 Osteology of the Reptiles, Cambridge, Mass. 1925
Willughby Society, *Reprints of Rare Ornithological Works*, 12 pts, 1880–84
Wilson, A., *Elements of Zoology*, Edinburgh 1873;
 Leisure Time Studies, 1879
Wilson, E., *Birds of the Antarctic*, B. Roberts (ed.), 1967
Wilson, S. B., and Evans, A. H., *Aves Hawaiienses*, 1890–99
Wolf, J., *Poets of the Woods*, 1853;
 Feathered Favourites, 1854;
 Zoological Sketches, 2 vols, 1856–67;
 Life, by A. H. Palmer, 1895, including bibliography
Wollaston, T. V., *Insecta Maderiensa*, 1854
Wolley, J., and Newton, A., *Ootheca Wolleyana*, 2 vols, 1864–1907
Wood, J. G., *Homes without Hands*, 1866

Woods Hole, Mass., Marine Biological Laboratory, *Biological Bulletin*, 1(1899)–

Wyatt, C. W., *British Birds*, 2 vols, 1894–99

Wyatt, C. W. and Sharpe, R. B., *The Hirundinidae*, 2 vols, 1885–94

Yarrell, W., *British Fishes*, 2 vols, 1835–36;
  British Birds, 3 vols, 1837–43; supplements 1845, 1856

Youatt, W., *The Horse*, 1831;
  Cattle, 1834;
  Sheep, 1837;
  The Dog, 1845;
  The Pig, 1847

Zoological Magazine, 1(1833), all published

Zoological Miscellany, 1(1831)–6(1844)

Zoological Record, 1(1864)–

Zoological Society, *Proceedings*, 1(1830)–;
  Transactions, 1(1835)–;
  History by P. C. Mitchell, 1929;
  London's Zoo, by G. Vevers, 1976;
  The Ark in the Park, by W. Blunt 1976

The Zoologist, 1(1843)–

Index

Exploration, 111 ff, 157 ff, 175
Extinction, 98, 125, 129

Fabulous monsters, 13 ff, *15, 17, 28,* 29, 82, 99
Faunas, 3, 12, 35, 85, 89, 116, 119, 157
Forbes, E., 170, *171,* 175, 180
Ford, G. H., *173,* 176, *177*
Fossils, 9, *28, 29, 47,* 48, 77, 98, 125 ff, 135, 147, 158, 167 ff, *169, 172, 173,* 182
Fuertes, L. A., 185

Gesner, C., 14, 15, 44 f, *77,* 79, 81, 99
Gould, J., 3, 5, *20,* 35, 85, 158, *159,* 163, 167, 185
Governments, 59, 81, 82, 106, 157
Gray, J. E., 2, *3,* 23, 132
Grew, N., 9, *10,* 84, 87
Günther, A., 40, *41,* 45, 91, 132, 133, 171, 176

Holt, J., *7*
Hooke, R., 18 f
Horsfield, T., 135, 136, 161, 165
Humboldt, A., 136, 162, 176
Hunting, 19, 23, 31, 158, 164, *166, 183,* 185, 188
Huxley, T. H., 87, 173, 176

India, 2, *3,* 19, 118, 133, 135, 161, *162, 163, 164, 173, 177*
Indonesia, 91, 113, 135, *136,* 162, 164 ff, *187*
Inheritance, *181,* 182
Invertebrates, *24, 25, 30, 32, 34, 47,* 48, *52, 77, 83, 90, 92, 93, 97, 100, 102, 104, 105, 112,* 118 ff, *120, 121, 123, 124, 127, 139, 146, 164, 166, 169, 171, 179, 184*

Japan, 1, 19, 62, 91, *160,* 161
Jardine, W., *134,* 141, 180
Jerdon, T. C., 161, *162*
Johnson, J., 78 f
Journals, 3, 7, 9, 53, 55 ff, *57, 58,* 82, *83,* 84, 85, 144 ff, 176, 182

Kirby, W., 119, *120,* 122, 157

Lear, E., 11, *21,* 23, 85, 141 f, 180
Lewin, W., 89, *90,* 118
Linnaeus, C., 3, 9, 72, 73, 74, 87, 94, 99, 111, 122, 132, 148
Lister, M., 92, 98

MacGillivray, W., 5, 141, 180
Mantell, G., *28,* 29, 129, 167
Mechanism, 102, 175
Medicine, 7, 87, 148

Merian, M. S., 79, 91, *92*
Microscopes, 6, 18 f, 69 f, *70,* 82, 103, 174 f, 182
Miller, J. S., *30,* 129
Montagu, G., *97*
Müller, J., 174, 176, 180, 182
Murchison, R. I., 157, 168, *169,* 170
Museums, *8,* 9, *10,* 72, 99, 119, 129, 135, 138, 148, 161, 170, 172, 176

Naming, 3, 74
Natural theology, 14, 96, *97,* 119, 125, 144, 167 f, 173 f
Newton, A., xii, *67,* 176
Nitzsch, C. L., *140,* 141, 180

Oriental artists, xii, 2, *3,* 19, *136,* 161
Owen, R., *24,* 156, 158, 168, 172 ff, 180

Pallas, P. S., 111, 116
Parkinson, J., 9, 125, *127,* 129
Patronage, 3, 7, 11, 12, *45, 47,* 59, 84, *100,* 111 f, 157
Pennant, T., 116, *117,* 157
Photography, 30 f, 66 ff, 182
Physiology, 174 f, 180, 182
Plot, R., *47,* 84, 99
Printing methods, 2, 38 ff, 71 f, 75 ff, 89, 141, 144, 147, 171, 188
Priority, 83 f, 87, 135, 168
Progress, 38 ff, 156
Publication in parts, 82, 85 ff

Raffles, S., 11, 135
Ray, J., 26, 75, 78 f, 82, 84, 87, 96, 99
Realism, xii, 12, 23, 26, 29, 39, 45 f
Renaissance, 12, 38, 44, 75 f
Richardson, J., *46,* 59, 119, 157
Russia, 106, 111, 116, 168, 170, *181*

Scientific societies, 3, 7, 9, 53 ff, 71, 75 f, 82, 98, 111, 119, 144 ff
Shaw, G., *147,* 148
Siebold, P. F., *160,* 161, 185
Sloane, H., 9, 40, 89, 99
Smith, W., 126, 129, 167
Sowerby family, 42, 168, 178
Specialisation, 9, 89, 146 ff, 156, 168, 182
Stubbs, G., 26, *27,* 31, 101, 116, 141
Stuffed animals, 1, 11, 19, 31, 175
Subscription, 3, 84 f, 180
Swainson, W., 59, 67, *134,* 136, 157, 164, 176, 180
Swammerdam, J., 103, *104*
Symbolism, 16 ff, *17, 76,* 164

Thompson, J. V., *24,* 26, 61, 89, 131